THE STRUCTURE OF

ATOMS

Verne H. Booth

BROOKLYN COLLEGE
BROOKLYN, NEW YORK

THE MACMILLAN COMPANY, NEW YORK
COLLIER-MACMILLAN LIMITED, LONDON

Second Printing, 1967

Library of Congress catalog card number: 63–21226

THE MACMILLAN COMPANY, NEW YORK
COLLIER-MACMILLAN CANADA, LTD., TORONTO

Printed in the United States of America

PREFACE

It is the hope of the author that this book will appeal both to the intelligent layman who desires to add to his present limited knowledge of atoms, and to the student who is majoring or plans to major in any of the sciences. This book is not a popular version of that portion of the history of science which deals with atomic structure; there is far too much science in it to be that. It is a book in science rather than one about science, and its objectives are varied.

For the college student, or even an above average high school student, the book should provide a coherent continuous story of how man unravelled the structure of the atom, a story that is gotten piecemeal, if at all, in courses in physics and chemistry. Better understanding of the various pieces is obtained when all are assembled to present a single coherent picture. Students majoring in any science need this picture, and they need it in association with the mental climates of the times in which the major pieces were developed.

The intelligent layman will not only increase his knowledge of science by reading this book, but he will also rid himself of many mistaken conceptions about what science is, what it can do, and what the responsibilities of the scientists are to society.

This book should make the point quite clear that progress in science is made only when the scientist has fruitful theories to guide his investigations. It should also aid in clearing away a lot of the confusion that is so commonly found among nonscientists concerning the nature of scientific theories and laws. It should also make clear the difference between the pure, or fundamental, scientist and the practical scientist (who is either an inventor or an engineer).

There is great need for a better rapport between scientists and intelligent laymen who have only a rudimentary knowledge of science. The gap between these two groups can best, in the opinion of the author, be narrowed by the nonscientist learning something about the laws and theories of science and the mental climate of the times in which they developed, and, also, something about the way in which changes in scientific theories occur. This is not to say that no effort on the part of the scientist is needed to narrow the gap. However, it is obvious to us all that any scientist, unless he is also a hermit, can better talk the nonscientist's language than the other way round. In any event, greater scientific knowledge will enable the nonscientist to better understand his daily newspaper.

CONTENTS

1. Introduction   1
2. Some Early Greek Views   5
3. The Transition from the Ancient to the Modern   10
4. The Periodic Table of the Elements   13
5. Some Basic Laws and Theories in Chemistry   16
6. Dalton's Controversy with the Law of Combining Volumes   29
7. The Kinetic-Molecular Theory of Matter   33
8. The Electrical Nature of Matter   40
9. A Digression: Facts, Concepts, Laws, Theories and Hypotheses   44
10. Faraday's Discovery of Ions   56
11. Evidences for the Divisibility of the Atom   69
12. Rutherford's Nuclear Theory of the Atom   86
13. Light as a Wave Motion   92
14. Theories of Light   106
15. Spectra   120
16. The Bohr Theory of the Hydrogen Atom and Its Modifications   135
17. The Wave Mechanical Theory   152
18. Building the Periodic Table   159
19. The Structure of the Nucleus   169
20. Conclusion   196

CHAPTER 1

Introduction

The whole of our physical and biological worlds consists of what seems to be a well-nigh infinite number of different forms of matter. Moreover, some of the differences among these kinds appear to be so numerous and so fundamental that any attempt to find any basic relationship among them seems futile. Consider, for example, a rock, a metal, a glass of water, a piece of wood, the petals of a rose, a piece of flesh, and the air we breathe. Primitive man explained apparent differences by acts of special creation by one or more of his gods. Such a hypothesis does not require that there be any relationship whatever and so does not encourage further inquiry. Primitive man also assumed that the gods who ruled his world never acted in any orderly fashion but always according to moods of anger or kindliness. Violent thunderstorms, earthquakes, volcanic eruptions, floods, droughts, or other catastrophic events were deemed evidences of their anger. Science could never develop in such a mental climate, for science has its roots in the assumption that there is law and order in the universe and in the firm belief that a particular set of effects is always preceded by a particular set of causes. All of us consciously or unconsciously believe likewise insofar as the routine aspects of our daily lives are concerned. Thus we never doubt that the sun will rise and set every day of the year, and at easily predictable times. We plan our lives accordingly.

However, in the less routine, sometimes unusual, aspects of our lives, most of us depart to some degree from these convictions. Some keep the sale of rabbits' feet and other good luck charms a thriving business; some search for four-leafed clovers or visit fortune tellers, astrologers, spiritual mediums, or others who prey upon those who are prone to invoke the supernatural to explain natural phenomena. Some primitive peoples try to cause rain by dressing and croaking in imitation of frogs, simply because they have observed that rain often followed an unusual spell of croaking by real frogs. To them the croaking caused the rain. More civilized people deride such beliefs, but may have no hesitancy in praying for rain and in ascribing any rain that may fall in the immediate future to the efficacy of their prayers. This tendency to ascribe certain events to wrong causes simply because the events happen in a particular sequence is common to all peoples of the earth. Even scientists are not entirely immune from it, but the true scientist is forever consciously trying to separate cause from effect, and both from accidental circumstance insofar as natural phenomena are concerned.

Man had no causes to ascribe, no problems involving natural phenomena to investigate, as long as he believed in special creation; things are as they are because they were created that way. Who was first to realize that there were problems concerning matter and its origin we can never know, for he left no record. Certainly the first real investigations came long after the first speculations concerning them. So far as we know from the written records the first speculations concerning matter worthy of our consideration were made by the ancient Greeks prior to 600 B.C. They had concluded that the universe was natural, that it was capable of being explained by man through the acquisition of observable facts and by rational inquiry without resort to the supernatural. Unlike the gods of other peoples of the times, the Greek gods were benevolent and undemanding; after creating the universe and presumably a set of laws to govern it, they left it alone. Their gods did not punish heresy, though sometimes the people did; Socrates was an example. There was no entrenched priesthood who had an abiding interest in maintaining the status quo insofar as their influence over the minds of men were concerned. During the first five or six centuries before Christ, these people of extraordinarily brilliant intellectual endowment had developed a sense of beauty and a deep interest in the highest forms of philosophy, literature, and art. They were aided by a land of great beauty with a marvelous climate, by their location adjacent to an oceanic highway which brought not only much trade but also much knowledge of the world to their doors, and by a system of abundant slaves which made daily routines easy for them and gave them time for the pursuit of an intellectual life. The same slave system, however, proved a handicap in the development of an experimental science, for it made a distinction between the labor of the slave and that of the master. In most cases experimentation involved labor classed as "slave," and so the Greeks did little of it. Instead they relied largely on reason in their search for reality.[1]

It is not surprising, then, that astronomical phenomena, including the nature of celestial matter, and mathematics were the first to be developed; neither required nor permitted experimentation. The Greeks and other peoples living in the eastern Mediterranean and the Middle East long had been intrigued by the heavens. The distinction between the "fixed" stars and the wandering stars (planets) were probably made by shepherds guarding their flocks during the clear nights in these dry areas where the stars appear to shine in far greater numbers and with a brilliance far surpassing that in humid climates. The concept of the earth as a celestial body, one of several planets revolving about the sun, would have been fantastic to them, even as it would be to us if we had not been taught otherwise. The separation of the sun's yearly *apparent* motion from its daily *apparent* motion across the sky is a sophisticated piece of scientific analysis accomplished only a few hundred years ago. The idea that these heavenly bodies could be made of the same kinds of matter found on earth would have seemed equally fantastic to early man, even as it did to most of his descendants right down to the beginning of modern times. In time, man turned his attention from idle speculation about the nature of celestial matter to the more profitable one of the nature of earthly matter and to the changes that could be observed to take place in it.

The changes wrought during the process of burning and through such arts as cooking, fermenting fruit juices, smelting metals, and making earthen vessels and glass must have caused thoughtful minds to consider the nature of these changes in matter long before written records were made. Further evidence that matter could change from one form to another arose from observations of the cyclic sequences that all life, plant or animal, go

[1] Plato considered experimentation a base mechanical art.

through. These sequences involve synthesis of air, earth, and water during life and decomposition of the life substances back to air, earth, and water after death. It should not therefore surprise us that these three substances played an important role in the speculations of the ancient Greeks about the composition of matter.

CHAPTER 2

Some Early Greek Views

As we have already intimated, the Greek natural philosophers attempted to replace the mystical, supernatural view of matter with a rational, naturalistic one capable of being expressed in simple terms. In doing so they discussed such problems as matter's reality and permanence, its relationship to empty space, and the number of kinds of primary (elemental) matter. The aforementioned sequential changes during life and after death led the Greeks to a realization of the indestructibility of matter. Further reasoning caused some of them to conclude that matter had always existed. Parmenides (*ca.* 480 B.C.) stated the extreme of this viewpoint by arguing that creation is impossible because something cannot be conceived to arise from nothing. Conversely, destruction is impossible because something cannot vanish into nothingness. Moreover, change is impossible because one thing cannot arise from another that is unlike it. To avoid contradictions with what we observe, he was forced to conclude that what we see or think we see in nature are false impressions given us by our senses. Thus our senses cannot lead us to the truth, and what is inconceivable is impossible even if our senses tell us that it has actually happened. Only thought is real, only thought can lead us to the truth. If our minds can eliminate all differences between bodies, we should be left with a single uniform essence (or element) which represents the underlying reality in all things. Other Greek philosophers had views that differed from those of Parmenides in varying degrees, but all, or almost all, gave a greater role to reasoning than they did to observation, a practice in direct opposition to that of the modern scientist.

We should realize that none of these theories of the Greeks were scientific theories in the modern sense, for they had no definite experimental facts, no exact quantitative measurements on which to base them. Instead, they applied the rules of formal logic to their scientific problems, a useless procedure in experimental science where discovery is wanted rather than formal proof from accepted premises; matter is not obligated to conform to man-made rules of logic. Such reasoning may lead to the assumption of infallibility and discourage any inclination to check facts. Formal logic is not self-correcting, whereas experimental science is. Hence these Greek theories, arrived at by the processes of reasoning alone, did not have to stand the test of future experiments and observations or serve as guides in the study and prediction of new phenomena. To them a theory of matter, or any other theory concerning natural phenomena, had to fit into and harmonize with other parts of a comprehensive philosophic-religious system that embraced the whole cosmic scheme of things. The worthwhileness of the theory did not depend on observable facts but on how good the fit; if an observable fact was in conflict with the scheme or any part of it, they ignored the fact rather than altered the scheme. Facts were not supreme arbiters of theories as they are today. A Greek theory could be upset and replaced only if some rival philosopher founded a whole new cosmic scheme more appealing to the minds of his contemporaries. (This last statement is, of course, a generalization that does not hold in every case. For example, the Greek astronomers rejected a moving earth–stationary sun hypothesis because they could observe neither stellar parallax [1] nor phases of Venus with the naked eye. There is no certainty, however, that they would have accepted such a hypothesis even if they could have made these observations, particularly if the hypothesis was in direct conflict with their particular philosophic-religious scheme.)

Thales (640?–546? B.C.) was the first important Greek scientist of record to speculate about the composition of matter. He noted that in both the synthesis during life and the decomposition

---

[1] Parallax is the *apparent* change of position of one object with respect to another due to the motion of the observer. Those stars that we can see every night of the year are not observed to change their positions with respect to one another as our observation post (the earth) moves in its orbit about the sun. They, of course, do apparently change their positions, but they are so far away that detection by the naked eye is impossible.

after death water appeared to be most importantly involved. He therefore assumed that it was the essence of all things, i.e., that it was the primary element. Somewhat later Anaximenes (died *ca.* 525 B.C.) chose air as his primary element. He thought it became fire when rarefied, water when first condensed, and earth upon further condensation. Heraclitus (535?–475? B.C.) thought that the primary element was fire. Pythagoras (582?–507? B.C.) and his followers forsook the concept of a single, primary element for one involving all three—water, air, fire—plus a fourth, earth. This concept, developed into a more definite form by Empedocles (*ca.* 450 B.C.) seems to have arisen through a misinterpretation of what takes place during the processes of combustion. The burning of any substance appears to result in the formation of the simpler substances, earth, air, fire, and water, which the Pythagoreans considered to be the primary elements. This concept, while not at all true, is far from being silly. Consider the burning of a green pine log. As it is heated, water may be observed to ooze from its ends and boil off into the atmosphere; smoke—which was thought to be a kind of "air"—is seen to rise and vanish; the flames are seen by their own light as they leap upward and vanish; and the ashy residue is of the nature of earth. The water was believed to have combined with fire to form what we now call "water vapor" which disappeared upward. Later this vapor would lose its fire, condense to become water again, and fall as rain. Thus water, the flames (fire), and the smoke (a kind of air) were thought to be driven out of the wood as it burned, leaving its content of earth (the ashes) behind. Every kind and form of matter was postulated to consist of one or more of these four primary (elemental) kinds of matter mixed in one of an infinite number of proportions.

Later, Aristotle explained gravity by assuming that each of the four elements had a natural home to which it returned when free to do so. For fire and air this home was above the earth, and so the flames and the smoke leaped upward; for earth and water it was on or in the earth. Fire added to water changed the latter to a vapor which rose upwards because the fire in it controlled its behavior. When the vapor lost its fire, it became water again which fell to its natural home as rain. A stone, assumed to consist largely of earth, thrown into the air, returned to its natural home by falling back to earth. Matter resisted any attempt to move it from its natural home. A big stone was more difficult to lift than a small one because there was a greater quantity of matter to resist.

This Pythagorean theory of combustion, developed, extended, and altered to fit rather neatly into Aristotle's orderly and harmonious philosophic-religious system of the universe, gave rise to the first great guiding principle of both alchemy and chemistry. If all matter consisted of these four elements mixed in various proportions, then it should be possible to change one substance into another, e.g., to change the baser metals like iron or lead into gold, if a method of properly altering these proportions could be discovered. Attempting to discover such a method was one of the chief concerns of alchemists for about two thousand years. Despite the extraordinary amount of work that went into the project, no advances whatever were made in understanding the fundamental nature of matter. The practical discoveries were also few. The project was doomed to failure before it began because it was based on a bad theory. This failure and the reason for it illustrates not only the necessity of having a theory if advances in understanding natural phenomena are to be made, but also the differences between a good theory and a bad one. Good theories are fruitful and lead to new knowledge; bad ones are sterile.[2]

One of the once-controversial problems of matter other than the number of primary elements concerned its subdivision. There are two, and only two, possibilities; matter is either continuous or discontinuous. If it is continuous, then it can be physically subdivided endlessly without any change taking place in the composition or properties of the particles. If it is discontinuous, then physical subdivision eventually results in discrete (separate) particles that cannot be further subdivided without change in the composition or properties of the particles. Particles not capable of further subdivision by ordinary mechanical means would today commonly be called "atoms" if the substance being subdivided is an element, and "molecules" if it is a compound.

The name "atom" was given to these smallest elemental particles by Democritus (460?–352? B.C.), or possibly by Leucippus, about 425 B.C. We know little about Leucippus (the older man) so we will talk about Democritus instead, remembering that much of what he taught was probably based on ideas advanced by Leucippus. Both were attempting to carry the simplification of matter

[2] See Chapter 9 for further discussion of theories.

to the ultimate. Matter was conceived to consist of particles (atoms) that were eternal and incapable of being further subdivided. Atoms of all substances were alike in composition, but one substance differed from another in the size, shape, position, or movement of its atoms. The atoms of a solid could only vibrate within the confines of extremely small spaces, whereas the atoms of a gas had, relatively, a considerable range of movement. Air had already been shown to consist of particles surrounded by voids, i.e., by empty spaces. According to Democritus voids existed about all atoms. The voids decreased in size from fire to air to water to earth. Atomic size was reached when there were no voids within the particle.

This was our first atomic theory, but we must not rate it with the much later atomic and molecular theories. It was not based on experimental facts, or on either qualitative or quantitative data, nor did it have to conform to or explain many isolated or interconnected facts and relations which had previously been established or discovered. Moreover, it did not have to meet the test of future experiments or serve as a guide in the further study of matter and in the prediction of new phenomena. In modern terminology we wouldn't even call it a theory; it is more properly called a speculation, for it was the product of imaginative minds alone. Its success or failure among other intellectuals of the time rested on how well it fitted into whatever philosophical system of the universe was dominant among them at the time.

A fine example of this attitude is given by Aristotle's rejection of Democritus' atomic theory because its consequences did not agree with his other ideas of nature. According to Democritus heavier atoms would fall faster in a vacuum than lighter ones. Aristotle believed that they would fall equally fast, but since this was inconceivable, a vacuum was impossible. He therefore rejected the concept of a void, and with it the whole atomic theory. Instead, he accepted the Pythagorean concept of four elements and, as we have already stated, developed it further.

Aristotle (384–322 B.C.) was the greatest collector and systematizer of knowledge in the ancient world. His works form an encyclopedia of ancient Greek learning. He probably made real contributions to all subjects he wrote about except physics and astronomy, where he was about as wrong as a man of learning could be. His best scientific work was done in the field of biology.

CHAPTER 3

The Transition from the Ancient to the Modern

The Aristotelian view of matter persisted for nearly two thousand years. The Romans accepted it along with most other aspects of Greek learning but added little of their own. The Romans had a utilitarian ("What use can be made of it?") philosophy toward science. New ideas never develop when men's minds are ruled by such an attitude, for how can one know the use of an idea in advance of its development? Rome declined when the barbarian hordes overran western Europe, causing the whole Western intellectual world to collapse. The writings of the Greek men of learning were hidden or lost. There was little or nothing to fill the void; it took centuries for another intellectual world to rise. Meanwhile the Christianization of Europe took place; with it came a literal interpretation of the Bible and a firm belief that the day of judgment and the second coming of Christ were very near. No interest was shown in secular knowledge for its own sake; the desire to objectively investigate natural phenomena disappeared. A great wave of intellectual darkness swept over the Christian world. Revival began in the twelfth century, being more or less coincident with the rediscovery of the works of Aristotle. This was a true revival rather than the birth of a new intellectualism, for the men of learning of the times, all ecclesiastics, took over Aristotle's system of physics and astronomy intact. In time Aristotelian science became firmly welded with Christian theology, forming a rigid structure in which the parts were so interdependent that to doubt one part was to doubt the whole. This served for a time to nip in the bud the newly developing interest in inquiry that was begun by Roger Bacon (1214?–1292) and a few others. This setting up of Aristotle as the supreme arbiter of scientific thought moved Bertrand Russell to call Aristotle one of the great misfortunes of the human race—through no fault of his own, however.

So firmly entrenched did the Aristotelian system become that more than four hundred years were to elapse before it was torn down and a new one built to replace it. The men chiefly responsible for the new system were Copernicus (1473–1543), Kepler (1571–1630), Galileo (1564–1642), and Newton (1642–1727). Only Newton dealt particularly with the nature of matter, and he left no record of having accomplished anything of importance.

As late as 1600 the concept of a single element was again advanced by the Belgian van Helmont, but this time there was some experimental evidence for it. He weighed a small willow tree and planted it in a weighed amount of dry soil in a tub. For five years he carefully watered it. Then he carefully separated the soil from the roots, dried the soil, and weighed both the tree and the soil again. The soil weighed only two ounces less but the tree weighed 164 pounds more—just by adding water alone. Knowing nothing of the process of photosynthesis, he concluded that the increased weight was due to water alone. Water, then, was his single primary element.

Among the first to break away from the four-element concept was Robert Boyle, the son of a wealthy Irish earl. Boyle (1627–1691) came very near to earning the right to be called the father of modern chemistry. However, he never could completely depart from all the ways of thinking of the alchemists (he still believed baser metals could be turned into gold), proving that no man can advance more than a limited distance ahead of the mental climate of the time in which he lives. He did, however, base his conclusions regarding the fundamental nature of matter on the experimental rather than on the metaphysical. He eventually arrived at the conclusion that elements, of which all bodies are made, are simple bodies of matter which cannot be resolved into other bodies of matter. Those which could be broken up into simpler bodies he called "compounds." [1] For example, water is a compound because

[1] In addition to elements and compounds matter often occurs in nature as mixtures of either or both. Thus air is a mixture cf gases, of which some

it can be broken up into the elements oxygen and hydrogen, which cannot be further broken down by chemical means. A hundred years later (about the time of the American Revolution) the great French chemist Antoine Lavoisier simplified the definition of an element by stating that it was any substance *not known to be* decomposable into simpler substances. Today we substitute "cannot be by chemical means" for Lavoisier's "not known to be" because we have far greater confidence in the analytical abilities of our chemists. In Chapter 19 we will give a quite different (but not necessarily more satisfactory) definition of an element.

---

are elements (chiefly nitrogen and oxygen) and others are compounds (chiefly carbon dioxide and water vapor). Most rocks and all soils are mixtures. Petroleum is a mixture of many compounds. A mixture can be separated into its components by mechanical means of one sort or another, whereas compounds can be separated into their components (elements) only by chemical means. Salt or sugar dissolved in water can be separated from the water by evaporating the water.

CHAPTER 4

The Periodic Table of the Elements

We jump temporarily nearly a century to about 1870. The list of elements had grown to some sixty-odd. Chemists had been concerned about the total number of elements: Was it finite or infinite? A believer in law and order in the universe had to believe that it was finite. This belief was supported by the fact that as the known number was increased, the more difficult it became to discover new ones. Attention was also turned to finding relationships among the elements, relationships that had to exist if law and order prevailed. Many elements had similar (but not identical) properties, e.g., sodium and potassium among the metals, and chlorine, fluorine, bromine, and iodine among the nonmetals. Moreover, many of the atomic weights [1] were close to whole numbers, too many to be due to chance alone. Yet a few were about as far from whole numbers as they could get; an example is chlorine with an atomic weight of 35.45. Many attempts were made to arrange the elements in some kind of order.[2]

Most successful is the scheme devised by the Russian Dimitri

[1] These are numbers which represent the *relative* weights of the various kinds of atoms. They are in no way indicators of the actual weights of atoms. For a more detailed discussion see pp. 24–25.

[2] Classification is one of the necessary activities of scientists, an activity that results in reducing chaos to order if it is successful. Thus the million or more different species of life can be grouped into genera, the genera grouped into families, the families into orders, the orders into classes, and the classes into a score or so of Phyla. Such a scheme is possible only because there are relationships as well as differences among species, relation-

Mendeleev. He arranged the elements in columns in ascending order of atomic weight, making certain that elements with similar properties were put in the same column. To do this he had to leave some blank spaces, spaces which he believed would some day be filled by newly discovered elements. From the physical and chemical properties of the elements adjacent to a blank space, he predicted the properties of the unknown element with what later proved to be uncanny accuracy. This feat was possible only because the properties of elements in a vertical column or a horizontal row varied systematically. There were some anomalies, for in order always to place elements with similar properties in the same column the order of the atomic weights of two elements had to be reversed in two or three cases. For example, nickel (Ni) and cobalt (Co) had to be reversed. A modernized version, called the periodic table of the elements, appears on the inside front cover. The term "periodic" is explained in Mendeleev's periodic law: If the elements are arranged in increasing order of atomic weights, the properties of the elements are found to vary periodically. In the modern chart the elements in the same vertical columns have similar properties and so are called families. Some of the families have names, e.g., the first, I A, is the alkali metal family, VII A, the halogen family, VIII A, the inert gas family. The horizontal rows are called periods. Note that there are only two elements in the first period, eight in the second and third, eighteen in the fourth and fifth, and thirty-two in the sixth, and that the seventh period is incomplete because we have run out of elements to fill it. This variation in the number of elements in each period probably caused a delay of several years in the formulation of the table. No reasons could be advanced at the time for either this variation or for the periodicity of elements with similar properties.

A few additional comments about this periodic table are in order here. You will note that in addition to the atomic weights which are given below the symbol for each element, there is a number above the symbol that might at this time be referred to as

---

ships that are somewhat less close among the different genera, and most distant among the Phyla.

No classification scheme is holy, however. One that serves one purpose may be useless for another. Thus new schemes are advanced from time to time, some of which may be improvements on existing schemes and so replace them.

its "serial" number. It is useful for quickly finding the place of an element in the table, just as a house number is useful for quickly locating its place on a street. Later we will learn that these numbers have a vastly greater significance. All of the elements above No. 92 have been artificially created by scientists in their atom-smashing experiments; they do not occur in nature, the reason for which will also be given later. Moreover, three other elements, 43, 85, and 87, do not occur in nature. The atomic weights of these elements are only approximately known and so are given as whole numbers in parentheses.

More important is the fact that this table includes not only all of the various kinds of atoms that make up the earth but also all of the kinds that make up the whole of the *observable* universe. This will probably seem an extremely dogmatic statement to most readers, but it will be fully documented later, by the evidences from atomic spectra.[3]

The attainment of basic understanding of atomic spectra is one of the crowning glories of science. It led both to the explanation of the regularities of the periodic chart by correlating them with regularities in the structure of atoms and to interpretations of the chemical behavior of atoms. To understand atomic spectra we must know something of the nature of light, which in turn involves a study of the elements of wave motions. Our story may therefore seem to be leading us rather far afield at times, but it is necessary if we are to achieve the objectives of this book. In fact, before proceeding further we are going to have to learn something about the basic laws and theories of chemistry.

[3] See Chapter 15.

CHAPTER 5

Some Basic Laws and Theories in Chemistry

In order to study these basic laws and theories we need to learn something of the elements of chemistry. A reader with at least a high-school background in chemistry may find it desirable to do no more than quickly scan the next few pages. However, he should not omit the whole chapter even if he is familiar with the laws and theories, for he would then miss the historical perspectives for the questions raised, the controversies stirred up by the theories offered, challenged, modified, and finally accepted.

Classification of Elements

Chemical elements, like everything else, can be classified in different ways. One is on the basis of their chemical activity. Of the approximately ninety elements that occur in nature, most are chemically active, some far more so than others. This we all know, for common experience has shown that some substances burn much more readily than others. A few, all rare gases—helium, neon, argon, krypton, xenon, and radon—were long thought to be completely inactive.[1] Another useful way of classifying elements is

[1] While this book was being written, xenon was discovered to be active enough to combine with fluorine, most active of all elements.

as metals or nonmetals. The nonmetals include the above rare inactive gases; the common active gases, oxygen, hydrogen, nitrogen, chlorine, and fluorine; the solid elements, carbon, boron, iodine, phosphorus, sulfur, selenium, silicon, arsenic, tellurium; and the liquid, bromine. There are about 3.5 times as many metals as there are nonmetals. In general, the metals will combine chemically with the nonmetals (rare gases excepted), but have little tendency to combine with other metals. On the other hand, many of the nonmetals combine readily with each other, forming such familiar compounds as water (H_2O), carbon dioxide (CO_2), sulfur dioxide (SO_2), carbon tetrachloride (CCl_4), and ammonia (NH_3). Cesium is the most active metal, fluorine the most active nonmetal; they will react with each other with explosive violence even at normal temperatures.

Chemical Reactions

The most familiar chemical reaction is that of combustion, a process in which oxygen unites with one or more of the elements composing the substance being burned. Thus, pure gasoline, a mixture of compounds composed solely of carbon and hydrogen, is consumed as the carbon unites with oxygen to form carbon dioxide (or carbon monoxide if the amount of oxygen is insufficient), and the hydrogen unites with oxygen to form water vapor. Here oxygen and the compounds that make up gasoline are the reactants whereas carbon dioxide and water are the products. The products have sets of physical and chemical properties that are completely different from those of the reactants.

As another example, consider the union of sodium and chlorine to form common table salt (sodium chloride—NaCl). Sodium is a soft metal that can be cut like butter. It combines with water to form lye. A piece put on your tongue would eat a hole in it. Chlorine is a poisonous, greenish-yellow gas which formed the mustard gas of World War I. If heated sufficiently, sodium will burn with a bright flame in chlorine, forming sodium chloride, a salt essential not only to good health but to life itself.

Chemical Symbols, Formulas, Equations

Chemists use chemical symbols for the elements (as in the periodic table, Table 1), chemical formulas for compounds, and chemical equations to express chemical reactions. Thus, Na is the symbol for sodium (from *natrium,* the Latin name for sodium), Cl is the symbol for chlorine, NaCl is the formula for sodium chloride, and the equation for their reaction [2] is $Na + Cl \rightarrow NaCl$. The advantages of symbols, formulas, and equations are so great that without them it is improbable that the science of chemistry would have made such rapid progress during the last 150 years.

Law of Conservation of Mass

Before the Pythagorean theory of fire with its four-element postulate was finally abandoned, there arose from it the phlogiston theory of combustion. This theory postulated that during burning a mysterious, nondetectable element called phlogiston escaped. The theory was accepted for a time, for it could explain many phenomena. It foundered, however, when the quantitative method was applied to the problem. Experiments showed that the *solid* residue left after most substances were burned weighed far less than the original substances, thus apparently supporting the phlogiston theory, but that if one collected and weighed the gaseous products produced, the total weight was greater than that of the original. Moreover, one found that the *solid* residue left after the burning of certain metals (magnesium, for example) weighed more than the metal burned. To explain this fact the phlogistonists had to assume that the phlogiston which escaped from burning metals had negative weight, i.e., it weighed less than nothing. This was too much for Lavoisier, the great French chemist who did most of his work between the American and French Revolutions. He made his claim

[2] The modern chemist would multiply both sides of the reaction by two, giving $2Na + Cl_2 \rightarrow 2NaCl$. The reason for this will become apparent later.

to fame by being the first to weigh painstakingly [3] every substance that went into a chemical reaction and every product that resulted from it. The failure of the phlogiston theory to explain this one fact caused it to be abandoned. In its place Lavoisier substituted our present oxygen theory of combustion. One of the results of Lavoisier's careful quantitative work was the formulation of the first great law of chemistry, the law of conservation of mass. It simply states that during a chemical reaction matter is neither created nor destroyed.[4] Lavoisier's ability to formulate this law showed that he had a necessary talent of every great chemist, that of being able to see the general principles which lie beyond the individual facts of a chemical reaction.

Some Early Consequences of Lavoisier's Work

Shortly after the beginning of the nineteenth century John Dalton, a self-taught English schoolmaster who devoted all of his spare time to scientific investigations, put forth the first atomic theory based on sound experimental evidence. The work of Lavoisier had given the chemists not only a new tool (the balance scale) and a new law but also a new theory (the oxygen-supporting combustion theory) to guide them in their experiments. The result was an enormously enhanced rate of acquisition of new knowledge, which in turn gave rise to the formulation of new laws and new theories.[5] The most important were the law of definite proportions, the law of multiple proportions, the law of combining volumes (applicable only to gases), Dalton's atomic theory, and Avogadro's hypothesis (to become Avogadro's law some fifty years later).

The Law of Definite Proportions.   We will not attempt to explain each of the above laws in terms a chemist would use, but will

[3] To do this he had to have adequate balance scales. Since there were none, he had to design them. His best could easily detect the weight of a small fraction of the tiniest drops of water.

[4] You may remember that some of the early Greeks stated the same principle. They had no proof, however, and they did not attempt to gather any. To them it was an interesting philosophical "truth" which needed no proof except that provided by logical argument.

[5] See Chapter 9.

instead be content with a simple example of each. The law of definite proportions (sometimes called the law of constant composition) formally states that elements combine in definite proportions *by weight* to form compounds. Informally it states that if analysis of one sample of pure sodium chloride weighing 58.5 grams [6] shows that it is composed of 23 grams of sodium and 35.5 grams of chlorine, then every sample of *pure* sodium chloride will show the same ratio of sodium to chlorine. The source of the sodium chloride does not matter. We can put it the other way if we wish: if in one experiment 23 grams of sodium will combine with 35.5 grams of chlorine to form 58.5 grams of sodium chloride, with neither sodium nor chlorine left over, then they will combine in these same proportions in every experiment. Many analyses of many different compounds and of many samples of the same compound obtained from various sources were necessary to establish the law. For three reasons it was not established without a great deal of difficulty. First, it is impossible to obtain pure compounds. Second, some elements combine in different ratios by weight to form different compounds, e.g., carbon and oxygen combine in different ratios to form either carbon monoxide (CO) or carbon dioxide (CO_2). Third, no analysis is ever exact because of inevitable experimental errors; this introduces some doubt about the reliability of the results.

The Law of Multiple Proportions. This law takes cognizance of the second item above, that some elements combine in different ratios to form different products. If we take a fixed weight of carbon, say 12 grams, then the weight of the oxygen necessary to unite with it to form carbon dioxide will be exactly twice that of the oxygen necessary to form carbon monoxide. The actual weights of oxygen necessary if 12 grams of carbon are used are 32 grams (for CO_2) and 16 grams (for CO). The ratio between these two weights of oxygen is 2 to 1. Iron will combine with chlorine to form either ferrous chloride ($FeCl_2$) or ferric chloride ($FeCl_3$). If we take a fixed weight of iron and combine it with chlorine to form the above two chlorides, we will find that the ratio of the two weights of chlorine is 2 to 3. In all similar cases the ratios are

[6] A new dime weighs about 2.5 grams. There are approximately 450 grams in a pound. If one wishes, he may substitute ounces or pounds or tons for grams throughout these examples.

simple, 2 to 1, 1 to 2, 3 to 1, 1 to 3, 2 to 3, 3 to 2, etc., and *never* 2.5 to 1, 1 to 2.2, 2.4 to 3.7, etc.

The Law of Combining Volumes. This law applies to gases only, because volumes of liquids or solids are not at all meaningful in chemical reactions. In form it is somewhat similar to the law of multiple proportions except that it applies to volumes rather than weights. It states that when gases combine, the volumes involved are in the ratio of small whole numbers.[7] Thus, one volume of oxygen combines with two volumes of hydrogen to form two volumes of water vapor; one volume of nitrogen will combine with one volume of oxygen to form two volumes of nitric oxide; two volumes of oxygen will combine with one volume of nitrogen to form two volumes of nitrogen dioxide; three volumes of hydrogen will combine with one volume of nitrogen to form two volumes of gaseous ammonia; etc. Note again that the ratios are simple; no fractional volumes to give complex ratios ever occur (see Figs. 1 and 2).

Dalton's Atomic Theory. If we accept Dalton's atomic theory, we find a ready explanation for the laws of definite and multiple proportions. The assumptions (hypotheses, or postulates) of his theory are as follows: (1) All matter is composed of discrete, indivisible atoms that can neither be created nor destroyed. (2) Atoms of the same element are all alike, *especially in weight,* whereas atoms of different elements are unlike, *especially in weight.* (3) In a chemical reaction atoms combine by weight in definite simple ratios. (4) They may combine in more than one ratio to form different compounds. (5) If only one compound is formed by the union of two different kinds of atoms, the ratio is always 1 to 1. (This fifth assumption turned out to be invalid. Dalton's insistence on it gave untold trouble to chemists for the next fifty years.)

This theory (minus the fifth assumption) has served to guide chemists ever since. Two of the assumptions have had to undergo some revision in the last half-century, but we should not let that detract from Dalton's accomplishment or from the usefulness of his original theory. You may think that there is nothing remarkable in the theory. Don't the valid assumptions naturally follow from the laws of definite and multiple proportions and the law of conservation of matter? True, but these laws are generalizations

---

[7] It is understood that when we compare volumes of gases, we always do so when the gases are at the same temperature and pressure.

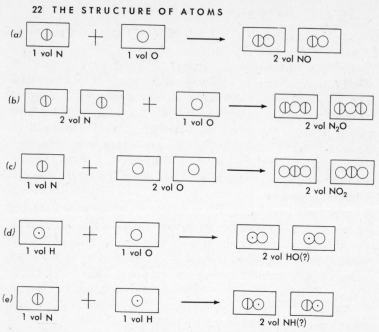

FIG. 1. *The Law of Combining Volumes as Originally Interpreted.*
The symbols within the rectangles are those used by Dalton to represent nitrogen, oxygen, and hydrogen. The numbers of volumes on both sides of the arrows were determined by experiment. Note that the volumes of reactant gases are in the ratios of small whole numbers in each case. Dalton's theory (as well as the law of conservation of mass) demands the same number of atoms on both sides of the arrows. If the elemental gases consist of monatomic molecules, experiment and theory cannot agree, and there is no explanation for the fact that there are two volumes of products in each case. In (d) and (e) the products are written as Dalton insisted.

made after the investigation of a limited number of chemical reactions; they are generalizations assumed to apply to all chemical reactions. But do they? Is there any reason why they should? Let us assume that you are a competent experimenter at the beginning of the nineteenth century, *before* the laws of definite and multiple proportions or Dalton's atomic theory were formulated. Suppose you were checking Lavoisier's law of conservation of mass. One way to do this would be to take weighed samples of compounds,

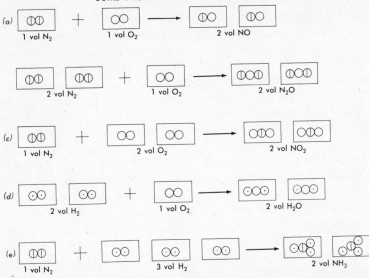

FIG. 2. *The Law of Combining Volumes Is Reconciled with Atomic Theory by Avogadro's Educated Guesses.* The number of atoms on both sides of the arrows become the same if we assume that these elemental gases consist of two atoms per molecule. If we also assume that equal volumes of gases at the same temperature and pressure contain the same number of molecules, the reason for the two volumes of products in each case becomes apparent. In (d) and (e) Dalton's formulas for water vapor and ammonia gas are replaced by the correct ones.

break them down into their component elements, weigh them, and then recombine them to form the original compounds and weigh again. If these final weights were within the limits of experimental error in all cases, you would conclude the law was verified. Suppose your compound was sodium chloride (NaCl), ordinary table salt, and that you decomposed three samples collected from different parts of the world. The results might be as follows:

Sample	Original weight	Weight of sodium	Weight of chlorine	Recombined weight
1	29.3 gm	11.5 gm	17.7 gm	29.1 gm
2	70.2 gm	27.5 gm	42.4 gm	69.8 gm
3	11.1 gm	4.35 gm	6.70 gm	10.9 gm

You would undoubtedly conclude that the differences between the corresponding weights in the first and last columns were due to inevitable experimental errors, so that your data were consistent with the law of conservation of matter despite these small differences. But would you look beyond to see if your data are consistent with a *possible* law of definite proportions also? You would be much more likely to do so if you believed in the discontinuous (atomic) theory of Democritus rather than in the continuous (nonatomic) theory of Aristotle, for there is nothing in the data which suggests such a law.[8] Your failure to look behind the data would be due to the fact that the mind normally sees only what it is prepared to see, barring things so obvious that only the blind would miss seeing them. If you are looking for snakes in a woodland lot, you are much more likely to see them than if you are merely taking a walk with no thought of snakes in your mind. Chance favors only a prepared mind, such as Dalton's. In his experiments he was looking for some all-inclusive principle or set of principles that could explain data such as those in the above table.[9] His atomic theory was the result. Once accepted, one could deduce the law of definite proportions from the theory (assumptions 2 and 3) if it had not already been formulated from experimental data.

Atomic Weights. There was little if any opposition to the theory. Chemists could proceed with greater confidence in their work of analyzing and synthesizing various compounds. They became interested in the two great problems that had to be solved before the science of chemistry could advance much further. These were the relative weights of atoms and the atomic ratios in each compound (in contrast to the weight ratios of specified masses of each compound). The atomic ratio in sodium chloride is 1 to 1, i.e., a single atom of chlorine to an atom of sodium.[10] We have

[8] However, if you divide each figure in the fourth column by the corresponding figure in the third column, you will get 1.54 in each case, thus showing that the ratio of the weight of chlorine to that of sodium in sodium chloride is constant.

[9] Note carefully that there is never an explanation in a scientific law.

[10] The formula for sodium chloride is $NaCl$ if the atomic ratio is 1 to 1, whereas that for magnesium chloride is $MgCl_2$ because the atomic ratio is 1 to 2, and that for aluminum chloride is $AlCl_3$ because the atomic ratio is 1 to 3. The precise method of determining these ratios is beyond the scope of this book; we will, however, discuss the problem after a consideration of atomic weights.

already seen that the weight ratio of chlorine to sodium is 1.54. It therefore follows that the chlorine atom weighs 1.54 times as much as the sodium atom. The *relative* weights of many different kinds of atoms were determined with varying degrees of precision in the first half of the nineteenth century by methods similar to that used above for sodium and chlorine.

Strictly speaking, atomic weights are not weights at all. They are simply numbers which indicate the relative weights of the different kinds of atoms. When we say that the atomic weight of oxygen is 16, that of sulfur is 32, and that of hydrogen is 1, we are giving no information whatever about the actual weight of any of their atoms; we are simply stating that the oxygen atom weighs 16 times as much as the hydrogen atom, and that the sulfur atom weighs 32 times as much as the hydrogen atom and twice as much as the oxygen atom. Hydrogen was [11] originally assigned a relative weight of 1 when it was finally established that it is the lightest of all atoms. The heaviest of any of the naturally occurring atoms is that of uranium with an atomic weight of 238. As the name indicates atomic weights apply only to elements. Compounds have molecular weights equal to the sum of the atomic weights of the elements making up the compounds.

Gram-Atomic Weights. The actual weight of even the uranium atom is inconceivably small, and that of the hydrogen atom is 238 times smaller. Yet if we have enough atoms of hydrogen they will weigh one gram. Let this number of atoms be represented by x. It follows then that x atoms of oxygen will weigh 16 grams, x atoms of sulfur 32 grams, and x atoms of uranium 238 grams. These *actual* weights of x atoms of these elements, weights that are numerically equal to the figure representing the atomic weight, are called gram-atomic weights. Table 4.1 gives the atomic weight of chlorine as 35.5 and that of sodium as 23. Therefore if you have x atoms of chlorine you will have a gram-atomic weight (35.5

---

[11] We say *was* because the use of hydrogen as the standard base from which all other atomic weights were determined was abandoned in favor of oxygen, to which an arbitrary value of 16.0000 was given. Hydrogen then became 1.008. In 1961 the base was changed again, this time to a particular isotope (for which see Chapter 19) of carbon, which is assigned an atomic weight of 12.0000. These changes (made to suit the purposes of atomic physicists) in the atomic weights of the other elements are so slight that we may neglect them.

grams) of it; similarly, a gram-atomic weight of sodium is 23 grams and is the weight of x atoms of it. The reader should never confuse atomic weight with gram-atomic weight.[12]

Actual Weights and Sizes of Atoms; Avogadro's Number. Do we know what the value of x is—i.e., do we know how many atoms there are in a gram atomic weight of any element? We certainly do, but how we know cannot be told until later. The number of atoms in a gram atomic weight of *any* element is 6×10^{23} (6 multiplied by 10 23 times). No one can visualize this number directly. Suppose we assume the age of the earth to be 5,000,000,000 years. Let us reduce it to seconds as follows: 5 billion years $\times$ 365 days per year $\times$ 24 hours per day $\times$ 60 minutes per hour $\times$ 60 seconds per minute. This will give us nearly 16 million billion seconds. The number 6×10^{23} is 6,000,000 times that big. Known as Avogadro's number it was named in his honor and *not* because he had anything to do with determining it.

How much does an atom of hydrogen weigh? If 6×10^{23} atoms of hydrogen weighs one gram (as stated above), then one atom will weigh $1 \div (6 \times 10^{23}) = 0.00000000000000000000000167$ gram. The mathematicians write this number as 1.67×10^{-24} gram.[13] This inconceivably small weight of a hydrogen atom raises a question as to the size of atoms. How much space does one occupy? For example, consider air, which is composed almost entirely of nitrogen and oxygen, whose atoms have nearly the same atomic weight. We will later learn that they occur naturally only as double atoms called molecules, so that if we have 6×10^{23} molecules of either we have twice that many (12×10^{23}) atoms. At normal atmospheric pressure and a temperature of $0°C$ ($32°F$) this number of molecules will occupy 22.4 liters (about 23 quarts). We all know that a room full of air is mostly empty space, for we can walk throughout it as if no air were there. Moreover, this 23 quarts of air can be easily compressed into a third that volume, and with somewhat

[12] A gram-molecular weight of a compound is a weight in grams that is equal to the sum of the gram-atomic weights of the elements composing the compound. Thus a gram-molecular weight of sodium chloride is 58.5 grams (23 gm + 35.5 gm).

[13] Any number can be expressed as a power of 10. Numbers larger than 1 are expressed as positive powers of 10, those less than zero as negative powers of 10. Very large and very small numbers are always expressed by scientists and mathematicians as the powers of 10.

more effort into a single quart. If we cool it sufficiently and exert enough pressure on it, it can be condensed to form a liquid which will have a volume of less than 2 cubic inches.

Suppose we have a box with this volume of 22.4 liters that is completely empty, even of air; i.e., the box encloses a perfect vacuum. Now suppose we make a tiny hole in the box, a hole just big enough to admit 1,000,000 molecules of air per second. Let us assume that air continues to enter the box at this rate until its density in the box is the same as it is in the normal atmosphere outside the box, i.e., until 6×10^{23} molecules (12×10^{23} atoms) have entered the box. How long would it take? The answer is 20 billion years! [14]

Atomic Ratios

We return now to the second of the problems of prime importance to chemistry, that of atomic ratios. We have already stated that we will not delve into the methods by which these ratios were obtained. We will accept them without proof. Mingled with the concept of atomic ratios is the concept of valence, which we will define at this time as the *combining capacity of atoms*. Atoms which have the smallest combining capacity are said to have a valence of 1. Others have a valence of 2, 3, or 4, but rarely higher. Note that valences must be restricted to integral (whole) numbers if the assumption of the atomic theory that states that atoms are indivisible is accepted. The concept of valence is incompatible with any nonatomic theory of matter.

Once the valence of one or two highly active elements has been determined to be 1, then it is comparatively easy to determine the

---

[14] One million is 10^6. At the rate of 10^6 molecules per second, it will take

$$\frac{6 \times 10^{23} \text{ mol}}{10^6 \text{ mol/sec}} = 6 \times 10^{17} \text{ sec}$$

There are a bit over 30,000,000 seconds (3×10^7 seconds) in a year. The number of years is

$$\frac{6 \times 10^{17} \text{ sec}}{3 \times 10^7 \text{ sec/yr}} = 2 \times 10^{10} \text{ yr} = 20 \text{ billion yr}$$

valence of other elements. Suppose the valence of chlorine is 1 (which it is). Then the valence of Na is also 1 if the atomic ratio in NaCl is 1 to 1. It follows that the valence of Mg (magnesium) in $MgCl_2$ is 2 (if the atomic ratio is 1 to 2) and that of Al (aluminum) in $AlCl_3$ is 3 (if the atomic ratio is 1 to 3). Now consider magnesium oxide, MgO. The formula indicates an atomic ratio of 1 to 1, but we have seen that the valence of Mg is 2. Therefore the valence of oxygen is also 2. And so it goes. Again we emphasize that the concepts of atomic weights and atomic ratios did not develop, nor could they develop, as long as the four-element concept and the continuous theory of matter were accepted. Man needs fruitful guiding principles, which the scientist calls theories, if he is to make progress in understanding the physical and biological worlds. The alchemists, lacking fruitful theories, made no fundamental advances in the understanding of the nature of matter nor did they produce much of practical value considering the great length of time and the enormous amount of energy they devoted to their work.

CHAPTER 6

Dalton's Controversy with the Law of Combining Volumes

We can now return to the law of combining volumes which was omitted from the above discussions because it does not follow directly from the atomic theory. Other assumptions need to be made to make it consistent with the theory. Dalton refused to accept this law because he failed to make these other assumptions or to accept them after someone else had made them, and so he could not reconcile the law with his theory. If you examine Fig. 1, you will see that in each case the volumes of the reactant gases (shown on the left sides of the equations) are in the ratio of small whole numbers, 1 to 1, 2 to 1, 1 to 2, 1 to 1, and 1 to 1 respectively. You will also note that in each case there are two volumes of gaseous products regardless of the total number of volumes of gaseous reactants. The law simply takes cognizance of these experimental facts: *When two or more gases take part in a chemical reaction, the volumes of both the reactants and the products are in the ratio of small whole numbers* if the reactant gases are at the same temperature and pressure. It was the data on the right side of the equation that bothered Dalton. Why always two volumes? More pertinently, why two volumes in any case? Why not just one? If one atom of oxygen combined with one atom of nitrogen form one molecule of nitric oxide (NO), why shouldn't one volume of oxygen

combine with one volume of hydrogen to produce one volume
of HO?

The great trouble was that the nature of a gas was not understood
at the time. Let us talk about particles rather than atoms or molecules, with the understanding that a particle may be either an atom
or a molecule. Dalton assumed that the particles of a gas were
atoms, an assumption that makes the problem unsolvable. Amadeus
Avogadro, an Italian lawyer who was pursuing science as a hobby,
made two educated guesses. The first, known at the time as Avogadro's hypothesis, was that equal volumes of gases at the same
temperature and pressure contain the same number of particles.
His argument was based first on the experimental fact that the
volumes of reacting gases are simply related (law of combining
volumes) and second on that assumption of Dalton's atomic theory
that states that the numbers of the various particles in a chemical
reaction are also simply related. The simplest conclusion is that the
volume of a gas at constant temperature and pressure depends on
the number of particles in it. This is essentially Avogadro's hypothesis. This means that a quart of hydrogen at room temperature and
pressure contains the same number of particles as a quart of oxygen
at the same temperature and pressure. If we assume that his guess
is correct, we can rewrite the equations in Fig. 1, substituting particles (shown by circles in the figure) for volumes (shown by
rectangles in the figure). We will use the indicated chemical symbols for brevity. Thus

$$N + O \rightarrow 2NO \qquad \text{(nitrous oxide)}$$
$$2N + O \rightarrow 2N_2O \qquad \text{(nitric oxide)}$$
$$N + 2O \rightarrow 2NO_2 \qquad \text{(nitrogen dioxide)}$$
$$H + O \rightarrow 2HO \qquad \text{(water, à la Dalton)}$$
$$N + H \rightarrow 2NH \qquad \text{(ammonia, à la Dalton)}$$

Inspection shows that there are not the same number of atoms
on each side of every equation, an obvious violation of both the
law of conservation of matter and the postulate of the atomic theory
that states that atoms are indestructible. Avogadro corrected these
violations in his second educated guess when he assumed that each
particle of the elemental gases on the left is composed of at least
two atoms. This is done in Fig. 2. Thus, we write H_2 instead of

H, O_2 instead of O, etc. Rewriting the equations [1] to accord with this guess, we have

$$N_2 + O_2 \rightarrow 2NO$$
$$2N_2 + O_2 \rightarrow 2N_2O$$
$$N_2 + 2O_2 \rightarrow 2NO_2$$
$$2H_2 + O_2 \rightarrow 2H_2O$$
$$N_2 + 3H_2 \rightarrow 2NH_3$$

All discrepancies disappear; we see that the law of combining volumes is consistent with Dalton's atomic theory. Dalton, however, refused to accept this explanation, chiefly because doing so for the fourth and fifth of the equations meant giving up the fifth assumption of his atomic theory, an assumption which demanded that the formula for water be HO and that for ammonia be NH.

Most other scientists of the time, even those who were not wedded to the fifth assumption, also rejected Avogadro's guesses. It is interesting to inquire why. True, there was no experimental evidence to support Avogadro directly, but his hypothesis did explain the facts. The trouble was that his second guess, which stated that the elemental gases [2] consist of at least two atoms, was in direct conflict with another belief concerning gases. The modern concept of gases had not yet been developed. The cause of the pressure exerted by a gas in a closed container was thought to be due to the repulsion of gaseous molecules for others *of their own kind*. While there might be forces of attraction between oxygen and hydrogen atoms and between oxygen and nitrogen atoms, it was believed that a force of repulsion existed between one oxygen atom and another, one hydrogen atom and another, one nitric oxide molecule and another, etc. The experimental observation supporting this belief was that it takes a force to compress a gas, a force sufficiently great

[1] Note the difference between the figures that are subscripts and those that are coefficients. The subscripts in the cases shown apply only to the particular atoms, i.e., the subscript 2 in H_2 means that two atoms of hydrogen form a single particle of hydrogen; the coefficient 2 in $2H_2$ means that two particles of H_2 are present. H_2O refers to one particle of hydrogen, *consisting of two atoms,* combined with one particle of oxygen, *consisting of one atom,* to form one particle (molecule) of water. For the present all particles that consist of more than one atom will be called molecules. Thus all particles in all five of the above equations are molecules.

[2] None of the rare chemically inactive gases were known at the time.

to overcome these forces of repulsion. If such a force of repulsion existed, how could two atoms of oxygen get together to form a molecule of oxygen? Obviously they couldn't. Since at the time (*ca.* 1815) no one could offer any other explanation for the necessity of a force to compress a gas, Avogadro's guesses were rejected and eventually forgotten. Yet every check made on the law of combining volumes only established it more firmly.

The rejection of Avogadro's guesses illustrate beautifully one of the reasons why new ideas fail often to win wide acceptance. They come into conflict with ideas already accepted, ideas which have more evidence (or what seems to be evidence) to support them or which are—or seem to be—more logical, ideas too deeply entrenched to be uprooted except by overpowering evidence. The last explains why young people can usually accept new ideas more readily than older people; the new ideas may not have to replace already entrenched ideas as in the older minds. Many new concepts win widespread acceptance only because their opponents eventually die.

The result of the rejection of Avogadro's guesses was a dilemma that proved almost disastrous to the atomic theory and to the whole science of chemistry. Since the law of combining volumes was correct, perhaps the atomic theory was defective. This also was well-nigh unthinkable for the theory had proved so highly successful in all other respects; abandoning it would slow the advance in chemistry until a new one was formulated to take its place. Many chemists were in despair, when nearly fifty years later (1860), Stanislaus Cannizzaro of Italy resolved it for them by resurrecting the forgotten guesses of Avogadro. These were immediately accepted, and soon became Avogadro's law; the science of chemistry was then ready to increase its rate of progress. The immediate acceptance was due to the removal of the original cause of the rejection in the intervening years. Physicists had formulated the kinetic molecular theory of gases, which, among other things, gave a different but acceptable explanation for the necessity of a force to compress a gas.

CHAPTER 7

The Kinetic-Molecular
Theory of Matter

The kinetic molecular theory of gases, which may be extended in some respects to liquids and solids, is one of the grandest conceptual schemes ever to come from the minds of men. It correlated an unusually large number of seemingly unrelated facts, observations, and ideas and in the long run helped to prepare the way for modern atomic physics. No man's name is attached to it for it was the product of many investigators.

Before proceeding further it is fitting that we clarify the distinction between atoms and molecules insofar as is possible at this time. In a general way, scientists in the nineteenth century thought of atoms as the ultimate particles of all matter, atoms being the ultimate particles of elements and molecules the ultimate particles of compounds. We now define an atom as the smallest particle of an element that can take part in a chemical reaction. The definition of a molecule in light of our present knowledge is made difficult by two facts. One is that some compounds, e.g., salts, are not composed of molecules [1] in the same sense that water, carbon dioxide, or gasoline are. We will avoid letting this difficulty bother us at this time by simply assuming that salts and similar compounds are composed of molecules in the same way that water is, but we will enclose the formula in quotation marks whenever we do in order to show that we are deviating from the definition accepted by chemists today. Our purposes do not require the rigorous definition of the

[1] Later we will learn that they are composed of electrically charged particles called ions.

chemist, and our explanations are much simplified. The second difficulty in our definition of a molecule arises from the fact that some of the gases which are elements [2] are monatomic (composed of particles that are single atoms) and some are diatomic (composed of particles that consist of two atoms). The monatomic gases are the rare, chemically inert (largely) ones, helium, neon, argon, krypton, xenon, and radon. Their atoms will not combine with other atoms of their own kind to form molecules and so exist in the atomic state only. They were of no concern to the chemists of a hundred years ago for none was known before 1894. The more common elemental gases—hydrogen, oxygen, nitrogen, chlorine, and fluorine—are diatomic. In the elemental state each exists as particles composed of two atoms, just as Avogadro guessed, and which he called "molecules." For the time being our usage of the term "molecules" may refer either to the molecules of the diatomic gases or the smallest particles of a compound which retain the properties of the compound. We now return to the kinetic-molecular theory of matter.

It may seem strange that a theory of gases, rather than a theory of liquids or solids, greatly improved our understanding of the nature of matter. We cannot observe a lone atom or molecule even with the highest-powered optical microscope ever built. We can, however, under proper circumstances, observe the behavior of masses of them. This is extremely difficult to do for matter in the solid state, less difficult for matter in the liquid state, but relatively easy for molecules in the gaseous state. While it is true that our senses give us much more direct information about liquids and solids, we can ultimately learn more about the fundamental nature of matter from a study of gases, chiefly with the aid of instruments. In part this is because their molecules act more or less independently of adjacent molecules, a fact which can be clearly observed in the case of colored gases. In part it is because they exert a pressure on the walls of their containers, a pressure that rapidly increases with increasing temperature in a closed container. They occupy volume which changes enormously with changes in either temperature or pressure. All of these changes can be observed by use of simple instruments.

The kinetic-molecular theory arose from two different kinds of

[2] The gases which are compounds present no difficulty.

investigations, one of which, as we have already stated, concerned the nature of gases; the other, curiously enough, concerned the nature of heat. This came about because James Joule, an English amateur scientist, became convinced that Count Rumford [3] was right in his hypothesis that heat was associated with the motion of submicroscopic particles of matter. To verify this hypothesis Joule had to develop a quantitative theory of heat. Since here on earth forces are always associated with motions, he wished to correlate the motions of the submicroscopic particles with the forces that act upon them. The fewer the forces the simpler the problem. Joule therefore began his inquiry into the nature of heat by studying gases and ignoring whatever small forces the gas particles may exert on each other.[4] Thus the two lines of investigation became intimately intertwined.

Assumptions of the Kinetic-Molecular Theory

Like those of the atomic theory, the assumptions of the kinetic-molecular theory are simple. It should be remembered that theories are never completely the product of the imagination. In most cases the author of a theory has the facts and observations of many experiments at hand. The evidence from any one experiment supporting a particular explanation may not be at all impressive,

[3] Count Rumford, born Benjamin Thompson in the colony of Massachusetts, was one of the most colorful men that ever lived. The accepted theory at the time was that heat, a mysterious, invisible, weightless substance called "caloric," was present in various amounts in all matter. Rumford discredited the theory in a series of famous experiments involving the boring of cannon, but could offer no acceptable substitute.

[4] Ice is a solid. It is reasonable to assume that its molecules are held together by forces great enough to allow little, if any, freedom of movement. When it melts, it becomes the liquid, water, in which we may assume the forces are not great enough to prevent considerable movement of the individual molecules. If we change the water to steam, the molecules have more or less complete freedom of movement; the volume has greatly expanded, so that the molecules must be relatively far apart. In other words, the forces between them have become extremely small in comparison to what they were in the ice, so small that at normal temperatures and pressures we can ignore them.

and perhaps other explanations may do equally well. Evidences from experiments of widely different sorts which all support a single explanation cannot be so lightly dismissed. The scientist could go on perhaps indefinitely planning and performing more experiments, some of which give new clues and some none. Such a procedure is time-consuming, burdensome, and expensive, the more so if many experiments produce no new evidence. The scientist therefore summarizes his evidences, and from them induces a theory. The theory consists of a number of reasonable inferences, inferences that are not proved beyond all doubt. These reasonable inferences are called assumptions, a word against which we should not be prejudiced. If the assumptions are valid, then the conclusions drawn from them should also be valid. The assumptions and the conclusions together form a consistent whole that we call a theory. The theory should be able to explain *all* of the associated phenomena. Let us see if the kinetic-molecular theory can do so.

The assumptions of the theory are as follows: (1) Gases consist of tiny discrete particles called molecules. (2) These particles are in constant *random* [5] motion. (3) The distances between molecules are, on the average, great relative to their size. (4) The molecules collide with one another and with the walls of their container; yet their average kinetic energy [6] remains the same. (5) The molecules exert no forces on one another except at the instant of collision.

The first assumption obviously must be, and is, consistent with the first assumption of Dalton's more general atomic theory. It is restricted to gases, and the particles are molecules instead of atoms. All of the pertinent evidence that supports the atomic theory also supports this first assumption. The second is easily checked; by using gases that have characteristic colors and/or odors, we can test the random motion of the molecules. For example, if we open a bottle of ammonia gas in the middle of a draftless room, ob-

[5] This is a very important word when used in connection with the motion of gaseous molecules. It means that on the average as many are moving in one direction as in any other. It also means disordered motions. Thus a steady wind is an ordered motion of gaseous (air) molecules. This ordered motion is, however, superimposed upon the random motion of the air molecules. Random motion may also be described as a sort of "aimless" wandering from "here to there."

[6] Kinetic energy is the energy due to their motion.

servers equally distant will all smell the ammonia at the same instant. The fact that the gas diffuses easily through the atmosphere is evidence of the third assumption. Moreover, the diffusion is more rapid if we decrease the density of the atmosphere and is slower if we increase the density (Fig. 3). The great compressibility of gases is further evidence that the molecules are relatively far apart. If the molecules are in constant random motion, collisions are inevitable. The collisions with each other without loss of energy mean that no friction is involved, so that a "bouncing" molecule bounces forever, instead of coming to rest as does a rubber ball bounced on the floor.[7] That molecules do actually "bounce" forever is indicated by the fact that molecules of air in a room do not

[7] The kinetic energy of the ball is transformed to heat energy by friction with the floor. This heat is dissipated to its surroundings.

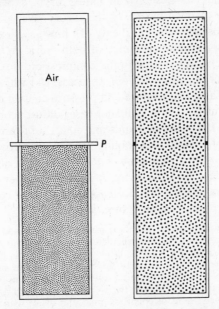

FIG. 3. *Diffusion of One Gas through Another.* Bromine, a reddish-brown gas fills the lower half of the container on the left. After the dividing plate, *p,* is removed, the bromine quickly diffuses through the air in the upper part to form a uniform mixture of bromine and air. If the space above the dividing plate were a vacuum, diffusion would be almost instantaneous on removal of the plate.

collect in a layer on the floor but remain more or less uniformly distributed from ceiling to floor, no matter what length of time elapses, if not disturbed in any way. The fifth assumption is that used by Joule to facilitate his inquiry into the nature of heat. (Its justification is briefly discussed in footnote 12.)

Further Verification of the Theory

The foregoing "justifications" for the assumptions were all known before the formulation of the theory. In fact, it is these observations, facts if you like, that gave rise to the theory. Other phenomena already observed in nature or in experimental work can now be explained by use of the theory. We will merely summarize the most important of them: (1) how gases exert pressure; [8] (2) why the pressure or volume (or both) of a gas changes as the temperature changes; (3) why the compression of gas is a heating process and its expansion a cooling process; (4) why equal volumes of gas at the same temperature and pressure contain the same numbers of molecules; [9] (5) why lighter gases diffuse more rapidly than heavier ones. Extended to liquids and solids we can understand the evaporation of a liquid as a cooling process, the processes involved in changes of state (from gas to liquid or to solid, and from liquid to solid or vice versa), the increase in the rate of evaporation of a liquid with temperature and decrease in the rate of condensation of a gas with increase of temperature, and so on.

[8] It is commonly stated that the gases have weight and therefore exert a pressure on a surface with which they are in contact just as does a solid resting on a surface, say a table. While this statement is true, it does not explain how the pressure in a *corked* bottle of air can be equal to that outside. Certainly the pressure in an automobile tire registered on a gauge has nothing whatever to do with the weight of air. Such a pressure is due to the incessant collisions of countless molecules of air with the inside walls of the tire and on the "diaphragm" of the pressure gauge. In short, the pressure of a gas is due directly to molecular bombardment, not to its weight. This pressure is, however, directly proportional to its weight. The reader is reminded that while air can be compressed into a very small volume, there are about 6×10^{23} molecules in each cubic foot of "empty" space in whatever room he happens to be in.

[9] Thus Avogadro's famous guess is explained. Upon its verification by experiment it became Avogadro's law.

Furthermore, the work of Joule and others who helped to formulate the kinetic-molecular theory gave us the first clear distinction between heat and temperature. Count Rumford was proved to be right in his statement that heat is the motion of submicroscopic particles, for heat *is* molecular motion. We must be careful here. Heat is *not* caused by molecular motion; it is not associated with molecular motion, but it *is* molecular motion.[10] Temperature turns out to be a measure of the *average random* energy of motion of molecules. The total heat content of a definite quantity of a definite kind of matter depends on three things, the number of molecules in motion, the kinds of molecular motion,[11] and their average random speeds; whereas its temperature depends only on their average random speeds.[12] Our theory also gives us an explanation of the concept of absolute zero, which is the coldest temperature possible. It is the temperature at which all random molecular motion ceases. Truly, the kinetic-molecular theory of gases and its extensions to liquids and solids is one of the greatest conceptual schemes ever devised by the mind of man.

[10] It should be clearly understood that no clear distinction is here made between atoms and molecules.

[11] Molecules composed of one atom each have only random motion, whereas those composed of two or more atoms have rotational and vibrational motions *also*. In rotational motion the atoms rotate about one another. In vibrational motion they vibrate back and forth with respect to each other. Both of these motions are ordered motions, not disordered random motions.

[12] We can now add to the comments concerning the states of matter given in footnote 4. We have stated that the atoms or molecules of a solid are held together by mutual forces of attraction between them. Our kinetic theory states that these particles are in constant random motion. When this motion is relatively small the particles are held in place, i.e., they have little freedom of movement. As they move faster and faster the temperature rises. The faster they move the more difficult it is for the attractive forces to hold them in place. When they move fast enough, these forces are largely —but not entirely—overcome; the substance melts to a liquid. If they move faster still, the attractive forces may be entirely overcome, allowing the molecules to break loose and wander randomly; the substance evaporates or vaporizes, becoming a gas. Any substance that does not decompose by heating may be vaporized if the temperature is high enough. At extremely high temperatures, compounds are not possible simply because the forces holding the atoms together are not great enough to overcome their kinetic energy.

CHAPTER 8

The Electrical Nature
of Matter

The title of this chapter indicates the reason for this seeming digression into the nature of electricity. In the time of Thales (p. 6) it was known that some kinds of matter had properties that today we term "electrical." Thales knew that a rod made of amber (fossil resin) which had been rubbed with fur would attract bits of straw or other light objects. It was some two thousand years later, in the time of Queen Elizabeth I, that the first new knowledge of this phenomenon was added. A number of new substances, all of them nonmetallic, were added to the list of bodies that could be electrified by rubbing them with another substance. Another hundred years passed before it was clearly shown that some electrified bodies repelled one another. Thus two kinds of electrification were recognized, one said to be "vitreous," because it could be produced by rubbing glass with silk, the other "resinous," because it could be produced by rubbing amber with fur. Bodies with vitreous electrification attracted bodies with resinous electrification, whereas two bodies with the same kind repelled one another.

In time, the term "charge" was applied to them, and Benjamin Franklin used the terms "positive" and "negative" to distinguish between the two kinds. Franklin developed a theory, as follows: Nonelectrified bodies were said to be neutral; they possessed a certain quantity of a mysterious invisible "electrical fluid" which we now call charge. The rubbing together of two neutral bodies capable of becoming electrified (or charged) transferred some of the fluid (charge) from one body to the other. This left one body with a deficiency of the charge and the other with an excess of charge.

Note carefully that charges are not created by rubbing; they are only transferred, or separated. Metallic bodies can be charged only if they are insulated from their surroundings, because charges are free to move in them; i.e., they are good conductors of electricity, and hence charges will escape if there is a path for them to follow. The best conductors are gold, silver, copper, and aluminum. Charges are not free to move in insulators, and hence a charge can readily accumulate on them. All nonmetals, including gases, are good insulators, some being better than others. Pure water is a nonconductor, but impurities, e.g., salt, in it may make it a good conductor. Some substances that are good insulators when dry become good conductors when wet. The charges on an insulated conductor tend to distribute themselves evenly over the surface because like charges repel one another. However, if the conductor has points or edges, the charges tend to accumulate on them and are repelled off into the atmosphere.[1] Charges on an insulator stay more or less "put." The reasons for this will become apparent later.

Since like charges repel, it is seen that in a conductor charges will flow from a region of excess to a region deficient in charge. We might therefore expect that if the two terminals (poles) of a battery are connected by a conductor that the charges should flow from the positive pole to the negative. However, when Franklin applied the terms "negative" and "positive." he had no way of knowing which pole of a battery (if batteries had then existed) contained the excess and which had the deficiency. He therefore had to guess. He guessed that rubbing glass with silk left the glass with an excess of charge, whereas rubbing amber with fur left the amber with a deficiency. Unfortunately he guessed wrong, so that in a battery it is the positive pole that has the deficiency of charge, the negative one that has the excess.[2] We need not let this error bother us. Since the flow of

---

[1] Thus lightning rods protect buildings because the charges leak off the points into the atmosphere as fast as they accumulate.

[2] We still use the terms as Franklin defined them because of the confusion that would result by reversing their meanings. Practical electricians therefore still speak of the current (flow of charge) as flowing from positive to negative. The term "juice," used colloquially for electricity, is a hangover from the days of the electrical fluid concept.

electrical charges is not visible, as is a flow of water, all phenomena connected with current electricity can be explained just as well by Franklin's assumptions as they can by the reverse. In fact, in the electricity commonly used by all Americans (except that generated by batteries), the current is alternating current; i.e., it flows first in one direction and then the other, reversing 120 times per second.

We have implied that charges do not move on an insulator, from which you might infer that there is no limit to the quantity of charge that can be put on one. This is not true, for like charges repel one another. Therefore, as the density of charge increases, more and more charges are repelled (or leak) from the insulator into the atmosphere until an equilibrium is reached, i.e., until as many leak off as are put on. The same is true of an isolated, insulated metallic conductor. However, if such a highly charged conductor is brought close to an uncharged conductor, particularly to one that is grounded, a spark may be observed to jump across the gap between them.[3] The spark is the visible and audible evidence of a momentary noisy and riotous transfer of charges from the charged to the uncharged body. This is static electricity. If, instead, we connect the two conductors by a wire, then the charges will move through the wire in a quiet, orderly manner. This is current electricity.

Matter, then, is electrical in nature. A question arises. What is the relationship between these electrical properties and atoms or molecules? You will note that we have not yet stated just what a charge is. Could these charges be physical entities, mysterious and weightless? Until the latter part of the nineteenth century most scientists had little trouble in believing in one or more of such entities, called "imponderables," because their properties were too subtle to be pondered by the human mind. One was phlogiston, which, as we have seen, was disposed of by Lavoisier. Lavoisier, however, had no trouble in believing in caloric and in the above-mentioned

---

[3] The physicist would say that the spark jumps because there is a difference of potential between the two bodies. The difference of potential is the consequence of there being more charge on one body than on the other. We have stated that charges are never created; they can only be transferred. It takes work to transfer them. Potential difference is a measure of the work done in the transfer; the more charges transferred the greater the difference of potential. It is commonly expressed in volts.

mysterious electrical fluid. Rumford discredited, and Joule destroyed, the concept of caloric. The discovery of the electron just before 1900 destroyed the electrical fluid concept. A fourth, that of the ether, about which we will have more to say later, was shown to be nonexistent about the same time. There is a certain amount of truth in the statement that the story of our investigations into the nature of matter is to a large degree the story of the development of these concepts and their overthrow. Before continuing the story of the investigations that led more or less directly to our early-twentieth-century concepts of the atom, we will take a much-needed digression.

A Digression: Facts, Concepts, Laws, Theories and Hypotheses

We have delayed defining or adequately discussing the terms in the title of this chapter until a number of them had been presented in enough detail to form a background for the present discussion. To have made this chapter the first in this book would have been largely a waste of time, somewhat like trying to understand the culture of primitive people without having any background of information about them. Until one has had experience with scientific laws, theories, or hypotheses, and has had the opportunity to discover, think about, and describe a number of them, and until one has some knowledge of the mental climate of the time in which a a theory, law, or hypothesis was developed, true understanding of them cannot be hoped for.

This is not to imply that all those reading this book have to do to obtain this understanding is to read this chapter. Only a start will be made at this time, a start that will not be completed even when this book is ended. It is hoped, however, that in the end the reader will have got rid of many mistaken notions about these terms, and that he will be able to distinguish between a law and a theory. It is also hoped that if he is somewhat disdainful of theories, as so many people are, and is prone to laud the practical over the theoretical, he will come to the realization that man's success in his upward struggle from caveman to modern civilized man is almost wholly due to the curiosity of a relatively few individuals and their penchant for formulating theories. Some peoples even today have never lifted themselves above primitive levels, because they lack something other peoples possessed. That something is not just scientific curiosity; in addition they have no desire to understand and explain those objects that do arouse their idle curiosity, i.e., to formulate theories concerning them. Without theories the search for new laws of nature would be a mere fumbling in the dark.

Theories

Essentially, a scientific theory is an explanation of some natural phenomenon or set of phenomena. This is not a complete definition (a complete definition is not possible).[1] A theory has been defined as a system of ideas or statements given as an explanation to account for a group of facts or phenomena. It has also been defined as a hypothesis that has been confirmed or established by observation or experiment, and is propounded or accepted as accounting for the facts. If we had to make a two- or three-word definition, we would call theories conceptual schemes—"conceptual schemes that have developed as a result of experimentation and observation and are fruitful of further experimentation and observation." [2] Conant says that the emphasis should be on the word *fruitful*.

"Fruitful" means that the conceptual scheme should suggest the making of new observations, new experiments, new explanations for inadequate old ones, or explanations for phenomena that have long gone without them. A good conceptual scheme will . . . "penetrate beyond the immediate and visible to the unseen, and

---

[1] The term "theory" is very widely misused, sometimes by people who profess to know considerable science. It is often used as a synonym for an educated guess. Sometimes a tentative answer to almost any problem, no matter how trivial, is referred to as a theory. In the minds of some, a theory is something that has not been proved. Often the word *theory* is used to refer to a hypothesis or is used improperly in place of the word *speculation*.

[2] James Conant, *Science and Common Sense*, Yale University Press, New Haven, 1951, p. 25.

thereby . . . place the visible into a new, larger context. For like a distant floating iceberg whose bulk is largely hidden under the sea, only the smallest part of reality impresses itself upon us directly. To help us grasp the whole picture is the supreme function of a theory. On a simple level, a theory helps us to interpret the unknown in terms of the known. It is a conceptual scheme which we invent or postulate in order to explain to ourselves, and to others, observed phenomena and the relationships between them, thereby bringing together into one structure the concepts, laws, principles, hypotheses, and observations from often widely different fields. These functions may equally well be claimed by hypotheses. In truth, we need not lay down a precise dividing line, but might regard theory and hypothesis as differing in degree of generality only. Therefore, at one extreme we might find the *limited working hypothesis* by which we guide our way through a specific experiment, placing at the other end of the spectrum the *general theory,* which guides the design and interpretation of all experiments in that field of study." [3]

We have emphasized the fruitfulness of a theory. Such a theory should correlate many separate and possibly seemingly unrelated facts into a logical, easily grasped structure of thought. A fruitful theory should spark the imagination to see if paths that have heretofore been considered entirely unconnected may not connect up with the new paths. A good theory should make it possible to predict specific new observable phenomena, and it may offer a solution to some practical problems. For example, the heliocentric theory helped to determine the exact length of the year and of the lunar month.

Let us consider Newton's theory of gravitation,[4] one of the most

[3] Gerald Holton, *Concepts and Theories in Physical Science,* Addison-Wesley, Reading, Mass., 1952, p. 138.

[4] The normal statement of this theory includes the Law of Gravitation also: Every particle attracts every other particle in the universe with a force that is directly proportional to the product of their masses and inversely proportional to the square of the distance between them. Mathematically expressed, the law is $F = G(Mm/d^2)$, where M and m represent the masses, d the distance, and G is a proportionality constant whose value depends not only on the units used to express M, m, and d, but also upon the measured value of the attraction between two masses of known weight and distance apart.

fruitful of all theories, in the light of these functions of a theory. Once the mathematics involved had been worked out, not only was an understanding of what kept the planets in their orbits possible, but also it became possible to map the orbits of undiscovered planets, explain the tides and the precession of the equinoxes, determine the masses of the earth, the planets, and the sun and calculate their densities, predict the shape of the earth and give a reason for it, understand the variations of the value of gravity in different parts of the earth, plot the paths of artificial satellites, and even understand why the high mountains are able to stand so far above the floors of the ocean basins. A theory that is not fruitful is a "bad" theory because it does not lead to further knowledge. For example, the theory that the earth was specially created as-is is a "bad" theory, not because it is not true, but because it does not lead one on toward a better understanding of nature. Such a theory is barren, for it gives a final explanation to all things, that they are as they are because they were created that way. A believer in such a theory has no incentive to investigate nature except to describe it, for he already has all of the answers as to why things are as they are.

It is difficult for the layman to understand that the scientists' criterion for a "good" theory does not depend upon whether it is true. If a theory is useful, adequate, and consistent with all of the known observations, the scientist does not insist upon "truth," for he knows that it is usually impossible to decide what truth really is in this context. He does, however, insist upon truth in his observations. He measures a theory only by its consequences— ". . . consequences in terms of other ideas and other experiments. Thus conceived, science is not a quest for certainty; it is rather a quest which is successful only to the degree that it is continuous." [5] If the viewpoint that the validity of a theory depends only upon its ability to suggest new experiments, which in turn generate new ideas, and so on, seems like a form of madness, we will have to let it seem so. For to seek to justify this attitude of the scientist would take far more space than we have available here. Suffice it to say that some theories that have been completely discarded were "good"

[5] James Conant, *Science and Understanding,* Yale University Press, 1951, pp. 25–26.

theories at one time. They became "bad" theories when they not only failed to account for new facts or suggest new experiments, but also became stumbling blocks to the development of new ideas, and hence to the acquisition of new knowledge. Eric M. Rogers of Princeton says that one needs to develop an educated taste for good theories just as you do for good cooking; in a sense, scientific theory is a form of intellectual cookery.

From what has been said above, one should infer that the scientist does not expect any theory to go down through the ages unchanged. Theories are always subject to change (by scientists themselves and not by others) as new facts and observations accumulate. Even Newton's theory of gravitation underwent a refining modification as a result of Einstein's general theory of relativity, a theory that predicted an extra motion for the planet Mercury. This extra motion, involving a slewing around the long axis of the elliptical orbit of Mercury by 0.00119° per century, had already been observed but not explained before Einstein. This refinement does not invalidate Newton's theory; nor does it make Einstein's theory better than Newton's. Actually there are still doubts and problems about Einstein's theory; but in general such doubts and problems about theories do not irritate scientists. They keep them in mind with hopes that the future will be more interesting to them because of the unsolved problems. For no scientist expects that the day will ever arrive when he has all the answers; he is convinced that new knowledge begets new facts and new experiments, which in turn beget new knowledge, and so on *ad infinitum*.

Hypotheses

Considerable confusion exists between the terms theory and hypothesis. In general, we might say that hypotheses are single, tentative suppositions provisionally adopted for use in devising a theory or explaining a certain fact or facts, and intended to guide an experiment if one can be devised. It is thus seen that the term hypotheses is much more limited in scope than theory, and that what many people refer to as a theory is really a hypothesis.

Facts

It is extremely difficult to state what a fact is. Since most physical scientists believe they are dealing with a real external world, they start with sense impressions as their facts of nature. In general, the facts of the physical scientist are the measurements he makes, measurements that can be checked and agreed upon by independent observers. If an experiment reveals unexpected and perhaps startling results, the important question asked of the experimenter is "Are your results repeatable?" Thus, science is in a sense self-correcting, for the scientist trusts only those "facts" that are the same in different laboratories, for different observers, and on different days of the week. Every scientist knows that sooner or later someone is sure to check and repeat his experiments, his observations, and his calculations, and so will most likely uncover any errors and self-deceptions. In one sense facts are more important than theories, for facts are the supreme arbiters of theories. More than one beautiful theory has had to be drastically altered or abandoned because of its failure to explain one ugly fact.

Scientific Laws

Scientific laws—sometimes called principles—are generalizations that describe the behavior of matter under a *specific set of conditions*. The physical scientist believes that there is order in the universe and that this order can be expressed mathematically; that nature works according to mathematical laws; and that his observations are best explained when the mathematical law relating the observations is found. From the time of Kepler and Galileo, mathematical methods have provided the best means for understanding nature.

Essential to the understanding of scientific laws is a recognition of their limitations. Thus, $d = at^2/2$ is true only in the absence of air resistance.[6] Boyle's law [7] does not hold at either very high pressures or at very low temperatures. Some laws are universal, or very nearly so. Such a one is Newton's law of gravitation. Another is Einstein's mass-energy law, $E = mc^2$.[8] Nevertheless, the most certain truth about scientific laws is that sooner or later some situation will arise in which they are found to be inaccurate or too limited. To the scientist this is no longer surprising, for matter is not compelled to obey physical laws. Unlike political laws there is never compulsion; yet the scientist expects matter to behave according to its laws, first, because the laws are an expression of the previous behavior of matter under specified conditions, and, second, because he believes that nature is orderly, not capricious. If the scientist finds that a law does not apply beyond certain limits, it does not mean that he is disappointed or that the law is a failure. Instead he tries to find out why, for beyond the limits of a law may lie new and exciting knowledge.

The Role of Speculative Ideas

Some phases of scientific thinking fail to fit at all precisely into any part of the general picture so far presented. One of these is the role of speculative ideas. Such ideas are the product of the imagination. They may be extremely useful if we bear in mind their status; how useful will depend largely upon the background of information and the level-headedness of the man begetting them. In general, we may say that only the well informed have the right to seriously speculate on any subject. An example is space travel, which is, or seems to be, just around the corner. It has become common for writers and radio or television commentators to comment confi-

[6] This is Galileo's law of free fall, which in words states that the distance a body falls freely to the ground is given by the acceleration of gravity multiplied by one-half the square of the time of fall. The acceleration of gravity at the surface of the earth is 32 feet per second per second. This means that speed of a freely falling body increases by 32 ft/sec for each second that it falls.

[7] The volume of a specified quantity of gas is inversely proportional to its pressure if the temperature is constant.

[8] See p. 181.

dently on these matters even though they know nothing about distances or conditions on other planets. Many fields of knowledge are today only in the speculative stage, but only the experts in those fields have the right to speculate seriously. In such hands promising speculative ideas may be sorted out and some means possibly devised for investigating them further.

The So-Called Scientific Method

There are few things, if any, about science more widely misunderstood by the nonscientist than those concerning the method or methods of science. In general, scientists are in agreement that there is no such thing as a scientific method. Few would agree that there are even a number of methods, unless you let that number equal the number of scientists. This is not to say that the methods of different scientists do not have some things in common. They do, very definitely so, but the term "method" implies proceeding step by step, and this is rarely done except by those who are tabulating facts.

The so-called scientific method makes little allowance for the "happy accident"—more commonly known as the role of chance. The initial observations leading to the invention of the battery, the discovery of x-rays, the vulcanization of rubber, the discovery of radioactivity, and many other things were made more or less by chance. Chance, however, favors the prepared mind, the mind ready to seize upon an unexpected observation and turn it to advantage. To one man the fogging of photographic plates kept in a room where a cathode-ray tube was operating meant (eventually) the discovery of a new kind of radiation; to another it merely meant that such a room was a poor place to keep undeveloped photographic plates.

To some scientists solutions came "in a sudden flash of insight," but only after the men had been completely immersed in their problems for some time. To most, however, if chance or inspiration enter at all, these are greatly overshadowed by hard work.

In any case, once a discovery is made, the good scientist subjects it to all conceivable tests, trying to ruin it, so to speak, for he knows that if he does not do so before publication, someone else will afterward.

Someone has said that the scientific method consists simply of observing and experimenting. This is woefully insufficient for it leaves out the most important ingredients of all, those of planning and pondering, doing and pondering, and just pondering. For you do not learn simply by doing, as some educators would have us believe; you learn by thinking about what you are doing while you are doing it. The planning is important, for a scientist does not just search; he searches for something. Otherwise he might pass by the critical observation without recognizing it.

Science vs. Nonscience

The various definitions of science and how it differs from other human endeavors would fill a moderate-sized book. Conant says that "Science is an interconnected series of concepts and conceptual schemes that have developed as a result of experimentation and observation and are fruitful of further experimentation and observations." [9] Einstein stated that "The object of all sciences is to coordinate our experiences and to bring them into a logical system." Niels Bohr made a similar statement when he said that "The task of science is both to extend the range of our experience and to reduce it to order."

Both of these latter "definitions" are much broader and far less specific than Conant's. Note the emphasis that Conant put upon conceptual schemes. These schemes, theories if you like, form the flesh and blood of any science. Without them, all we would have is a bunch of dry bones. The study of science in the context of this book is to a large and important degree the study of the development of these conceptual schemes.

One important difference between science and nonscience is

[9] *Op. cit.*

that in the course of time there has been accumulated a set of basic concepts, conceptual schemes, and physical laws that have been endorsed by scientists of every country. Thus, Kepler's laws, Galileo's law of free fall, and Newton's laws of motion and gravitation are acceptable wherever scientists work. This can scarcely be said of other human endeavors.

Science, more than most disciplines, is cumulative. By this we mean that in large part one man builds on the work of his predecessors; i.e., he begins where the others have left off. To do this he may repeat some of their work, but essentially his aim is to add to knowledge of the subject. Newton said that if he had seen farther than others it was because he had the shoulders of giants to stand on. In doing this, the scientist has no hesitation, if he thinks fit, in altering his predecessors' theories or laws, or even their facts and, more frequently, the interpretations placed on them. Note how different it is in the fields of literature, art, and music. Newcomers in these fields do not begin where others left off, nor would they think of ever trying to improve their works by changing words, adding brush strokes, or changing notes of masters like Shakespeare, Leonardo da Vinci, or Beethoven. Yet science is just as much a creative endeavor as are the arts, and the motivation is much the same. Some scientists have been just as willing to "starve in a garret" as any writer, artist, or composer, provided only that they could continue their work.

Henri Poincaré, the great French mathematician, supported this view when he said:

The scientist does not study nature because it is useful; he studies it because he delights in it, and he delights in it because it is beautiful. If nature were not beautiful, it would not be worth knowing, and if nature were not worth knowing, life would not be worth living. Of course, I do not speak of that beauty which strikes the senses, the beauty of quality and appearances; not that I undervalue such beauty, far from it, but it has nothing to do with science; I mean that profounder beauty which comes from the harmonious order of the parts and which a pure intelligence can grasp. This it is which gives body, a structure so to speak, to the iridescent appearances which flatter our senses, and without this support the beauty of these fugitive dreams would be only imperfect, because it would be vague and always fleeting. On the contrary, intellectual beauty is sufficient unto itself, and it is for its sake, more perhaps than for the future good of humanity, that the scientist devotes himself to long and difficult labor.[10]

Practical Science vs.
Fundamental or Pure Science

Many people are prone to laud the practical scientist, Thomas Edison, for example, while tending to scoff at the theoretical scientist. The practical scientist is trying to invent something that will be of some practical use, and this everyone can understand and appreciate. Far more difficult for the layman to appreciate is the work of a pure scientist on some problem that can result in nothing apparently useful at the time. Furthermore, he is amazed that the scientist considers usefulness as unimportant. The layman fails to realize that little progress in science can be made if usefulness is the sole criterion. Friends of Benjamin Franklin wanted to know why he experimented with electricity. "What use is it?" they asked. Franklin's answer is supposed to have been "Of what use is a newborn babe?"

At the time of discovery one can rarely predict where that discovery will find its uses. Because of Michael Faraday and Joseph Henry, both experimenters in the search for fundamental truth, Thomas Edison, the practical scientist (inventor), was able to invent the electric light bulb. Without the work of the pure scientists, both theoretical and experimental, the practical scientists would have nothing to invent.

As an outstanding example of the inability to evaluate the full significance of a discovery at the time it is made, consider the rather casual discovery of radioactivity in the 1890's. Out of it has come a tool for extremely effective research into the structure of the atom, the treatment of certain diseases, a method for estimating the minimum age of the earth, and innumerable other uses in biology, geology, astronomy, metallurgy, archaeology, and other fields.

[10] Jules Henri Poincaré, *Foundations of Science*, Science Press, New York, 1929.

But let it not be thought that the pure scientist seeks to justify his work through citing examples like the preceding. To him—and to you—it should need no such justification, for knowledge for its own sake is a sufficient answer. Or, as Michelson answered when asked why he spent so much time measuring the velocity of light, "Because it's so much fun."

CHAPTER 10

Faraday's Discovery of Ions

Current electricity was not known until some ten years after Franklin's death in 1790. Alessandro Volta's invention of the battery made it possible for a continuous current to be produced for the first time and so opened up new fields of research into electrical phenomena. By 1810 many experimenters were at work; new discoveries came rapidly. The greatest of these experimenters was unquestionably Michael Faraday [1] of England, who made many of the discoveries on which our modern electrical industries are built.

Faraday's first battery consisted of seven halfpence (largely copper) arranged in a pile and alternating with seven disks of zinc about the same size as the halfpence; thick paper moistened with salt water separated the metal disks from one another (Fig. 4). How such a device could produce an electric current is beyond the

[1] Michael Faraday was born in 1791, the son of a London blacksmith. He had little formal education. At fourteen he was apprenticed to a bookbinder. Michael became interested in physics and chemistry by reading some of the books he bound. When he was twenty-one, he attended a series of lectures by Sir Humphrey Davy, the director of the laboratory of the Royal Institution of London. He took notes of these lectures, wrote them out in fuller form, and forwarded them to Davy. They impressed Davy favorably; the next year Faraday was offered a job as assistant in the laboratory. Twelve years later he was its director. He remained with the institution for fifty-four years. He is best known for his discoveries of the principles of the electric generator and the transformer, and for the formation of the laws of electrolysis. His other accomplishments were far too many to list here. He was unquestionably one of the greatest scientists. Sir Humphrey Davy, who had made many important discoveries himself, was once asked what his greatest discovery was. His quick answer was, "Michael Faraday."

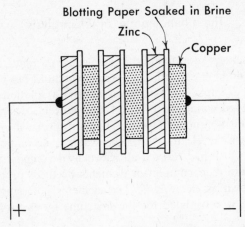

FIG. 4. A *Voltaic Cell (Battery)*. Alternating discs of copper and zinc are separated by blotting paper soaked in brine. A difference of potential develops between the zinc and the copper. If the two ends of the wire are connected, a current will flow for a time.

scope of this book. We will simply state that one terminal of the pile (battery) was negatively charged, i.e., it had an excess of charge, and the other terminal was positively charged, i.e., it had a deficiency of charge. This differential is maintained by chemical action within the pile (battery) until the chemicals responsible for the action are used up and the battery goes "dead." If we connect the two terminals with a wire (which is, in effect, what you do when you press the button of a flashlight), charges flow from the terminal with the excess to the terminal with the deficiency. If we attach one end of a piece of wire to the negative terminal and the end of another piece to the positive terminal, leaving the other ends of each free, many of the charges simply move out (because of mutual repulsions) to the ends of the wires; i.e., the end of each wire becomes a terminal of the battery. The free ends of these wires are then called *electrodes;* the one bearing the negative charges is the *cathode,* the one bearing the positive charges, the *anode.* Commonly, these electrodes consist of strips or plates of carbon, platinum, or nickel attached to the ends of the wires. No current will flow unless the two electrodes are connected in some way by a conductor.

The Phenomenon of Electrolysis

Experimenters soon found that an electric current from Volta's batteries could be passed through certain solutions but not through others. For example, as mentioned earlier, a solution of salt in water is a good conductor of an electric current, whereas one of sugar in water is a nonconductor.[2] In the process of carrying the current, either the electrolyte or the water is decomposed. Some compounds which had resisted all efforts to decompose them were broken up into their component elements by these processes, collectively known as electrolysis. The elements potassium, sodium, and chlorine were isolated for the first time by electrolysis about 1807.

How is the electric current carried through an electrolytic solution? The explanation of this and certain other electrical phenomena will be facilitated if we use modern terminology.[3] Thus we will substitute the word *electron* for the expression *negative* charge. A positive charge then becomes merely a deficiency of electrons, and an electric current in a wire is a stream of electrons.[4] If this definition is all inclusive, then it would seem that the passage of an electric current through an electrolytic solution must involve a stream of electrons. Reverting to our use of the term *charge,* we can say, more generally, that such a current consists of streams of charged particles which may or may not be electrons.

Let us consider an actual case in order to clarify the phenomenon. We will use common table salt (sodium chloride) as our electrolyte. A water solution of it would complicate the process, for sodium is highly reactive with water; the instant a sodium atom is formed, it reacts with water to form sodium hydroxide (lye).

[2] Solutions which will carry an electric current are called electrolytes. Solutions of salts, acids, and bases (e.g., lye) are all electrolytes. Some are much better than others.

[3] We will still use the term charge at times, usually to indicate quantity of charge. The practical unit of charge is the coulomb, equivalent to 6×10^{18} electrons.

[4] The electrons move continuously in the same direction if the electricity is d-c (direct current). Batteries generate d-c only. In a-c (alternating current) the electrons move back and forth through the conductor. In the United States, 60-cycle current is generated, in which the electrons change direction 120 times per second (twice during each cycle).

We will therefore use pure molten sodium chloride [5] as our electrolyte, for it conducts an electric current as well as does a water solution of a salt. For convenience of reference we will refer to the molten salt as a solution.

When the current is started, the two electrodes instantly become charged (Fig. 5), one positively (the anode) and one negatively (the cathode). We soon note that sodium metal is being

[5] Its melting point is about 800° C. (1475° F.).

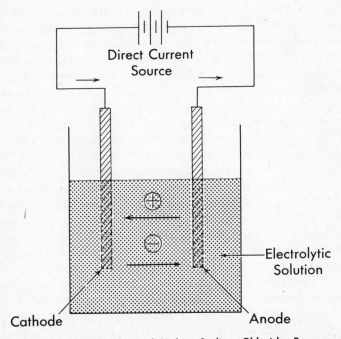

FIG. 5. *Process of Electrolysis of Molten Sodium Chloride.* Because of electrostatic attractions the positively charged sodium atoms (ions) move to the negative electrode (cathode) where they gain an electron to become neutral atoms. They are deposited on the cathode. The negatively charged chlorine atoms (ions) move to the positively charged electrode (anode) where they give up an electron to become neutral atoms which are released as a free gas. The electron given up is "pumped" by the battery through the wires to the cathode where it becomes available for a sodium ion.

deposited on the cathode, and that chlorine gas is being liberated at the anode. For this to happen particles of sodium must move through the solution and in so doing must carry the current. We must assume that the sodium particles move toward the negatively charged cathode only because they carry a positive charge. Similar reasoning forces us to the conclusion that the chlorine particles must carry negative charges. Faraday called these charged particles "ions," from a Greek word meaning "wanderer."

If we weighed both the sodium released at the cathode and the chlorine at the anode, we would find the sum of these weights to be exactly equal to the amount of sodium chloride decomposed. This proves that nothing has been added or subtracted; the sodium chloride has simply been decomposed into the elements composing it. If we wished, we could burn the sodium in the chlorine. Our product would be sodium chloride, and if we were careful enough not to lose any chlorine or sodium, we would find that the weight of this product equaled the weight of the salt decomposed.

It is apparent from our discussion of the direction of movement of the charges in the solution and our equating of a negative charge with an electron that the sodium ions must be deficient in electrons and the chlorine ions must contain excess electrons. Moreover, if our definition of an electric current as a stream of electrons is to hold here, the chlorine ions must give up their excess electrons at the anode, and the sodium ions must make up their deficiency at the cathode by gaining electrons there. Thus we see that the passage of an electric current through an electrolytic solution consists of electrons being ferried through the solution on negatively charged ions to the anode where the excess electrons are released and the chlorine ions become chlorine atoms. These electrons then travel from the anode to the cathode via the battery, where they are transferred to sodium ions to form sodium atoms. The battery acts like an electron pump, pumping electrons through the circuit. The net result is the transfer of electrons from chlorine ions to sodium ions to give us neutral chlorine and sodium atoms. By this transfer the compound sodium chloride is decomposed into its constituent elements.

One other question remains to be answered by the thoughtful reader. How do the ions originate in the first place? Faraday assumed that they were created by the electric current. Positive and negative charges and their behavior constitute what scientists of his time called electrolysis. It was natural then to assume that in electrolytic solutions these charges whose source was assumed to be the battery somehow attached themselves to the atoms, thus creating the ions. The current answer will have to await further developments in our acquisition of knowledge of the structure of atoms.[6]

The Law of Electrolysis

So far our investigations into the phenomena of electrolysis have been purely qualitative. This adds to our knowledge in a more or less superficial way. To gain real insight scientists have learned that their experiments *must* also be quantitative. Faraday's quantitative work, given below, resulted in his law of electrolysis, to which we will now turn our attention.

Note that in the above explanation it was implied that the number of charges (electrons) given up at the anode by the chlorine ions exactly equaled the number received at the cathode by the sodium ions. This is in accord with the concept that neutral matter contains equal numbers of positive and negative charges, and that these charges cannot be created, but only separated. In the process of separation it is obvious that the numbers of positive and negative charges that are thus isolated must be equal. Other evidence that equal numbers of Na and Cl ions are released at the electrodes will be presented shortly.

Suppose we let the current flow through the solution (Fig. 5) until we have collected 35.5 grams of chlorine. We select this quantity because 35.5 is the atomic weight of chlorine; thus 35.5 grams of it is one gram-atomic weight, consisting of 6×10^{23} atoms of chlorine (see p. 25). If we now weigh the amount of sodium that has been collected at the cathode, we will find it weighs 23 grams.

[6] Twenty years after the death of Faraday in 1867, Arrhenius, a Swedish chemist, suggested that it was the water that created the ions. He had evidence that ions were present in water solutions when no current was flowing. He was correct here, but we have just proved him wrong in his assumption that water created the ions, for there was no water present in our solution—we have used pure molten sodium chloride.

We note that this is one gram-atomic weight of sodium. It must also consist of 6×10^{23} atoms. We now calculate [7] the quantity of electricity (charge), i.e., the number of coulombs that passed through the system during the time it took to liberate the above quantities of sodium and chlorine. This quantity is 96,500 coulombs.[8]

If we run the experiment twice as long, twice the charge (number of coulombs) will be used and twice the weights of sodium and chlorine will be released. Other experiments confirm the fact that the weight of a *particular* element released during electrolysis is directly proportional to the amount of charge. Note the word *particular* in the above sentence. It restricts the comparison to the amounts of any one element, e.g., sodium, released by one quantity of charge and the amount released by some other quantity of charge. It offers no comparison between the amount of sodium released and the amount of some other element released; e.g., the amount of magnesium released by the same or any other quantity of charge.

Faraday, however, performed experiments to make these comparisons. One of them was to pass the same quantity of charge through a series of solutions. Figure 6 shows a setup similar to one of Faraday's. The four solutions are those of hydrogen chloride

[7] This is done by multiplying the ammeter reading, taken while the experiment was running, by the time in seconds that it ran. An ampere is a coulomb per second, and a coulomb is 6×10^{18} electrons. The principle in the calculation is the same as that used in determining the amount of water coming from a faucet; the total volume is the number of gallons per unit time multiplied by the length of time the water runs. The unit of quantity of charge, the coulomb, corresponds to the unit of quantity of water, the gallon. One coulomb is approximately the quantity of charge that flows through a lighted 100-watt light bulb in 1 sec.

[8] Since a coulomb represents a definite number of electrons, we can determine the number of electrons in 96,500 coulombs in a number of ways. If this number of coulombs will transfer one electron from 6×10^{23} ions of chlorine to 6×10^{23} ions of sodium, it follows that the total number of electrons transferred is also 6×10^{23}. Or if we can measure the charge on the electron (which we have been able to do since *ca.* 1905), we can divide this charge into 96,500 coulombs. Thus

$$\frac{96,500 \text{ coulombs}}{1.6 \times 10^{-19} \text{ coulombs/electron}} = \frac{9.6500 \times 10^4}{1.6 \times 10^{-19}} = 6 \times 10^{23} \text{ electrons.}$$

Moreover if we divide the number of electrons in 96,500 coulombs by 96,500 we will get the number of electrons in 1 coulomb. Thus

$$\frac{6 \times 10^{23} \text{ electrons}}{96,500 \text{ coulombs}} = \frac{6 \times 10^{23}}{9.65 \times 10^4} = 6 \times 10^{18} \text{ electrons/coulomb.}$$

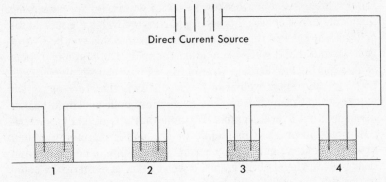

FIG. 6. Experimental Verification of Faraday's Laws of Electrolysis. Beakers numbered 1 through 4 containing HCl solution, molten sodium chloride (NaCl), molten magnesium chloride (MgCl₂), and molten aluminum chloride (AlCl₃) (with a mineral, cryolite, added to make it ionize), respectively, are connected in series with a battery and an ammeter (not shown). The same quantity of charge (number of electrons) pass through each beaker. The total amount is determined by the ammeter and a clock. The quantity of each metal deposited on each cathode and of each gas liberated at each anode is carefully measured. The data confirm Faraday's laws.

(HCl) gas in water (commonly known as hydrochloric acid), molten sodium chloride, molten magnesium chloride (MgCl₂), and molten aluminum chloride (AlCl₃).[9] They are connected in series with a battery and an ammeter (not shown) to form a *single* circuit, thus guaranteeing that exactly the same quantity of charge (number of electrons) passes through each solution. We include a "solution" of molten sodium chloride and let the current run until we have collected 35.5 grams of chlorine from it in order to make a direct comparison with the results of our first experiment (Fig. 5). Since we have collected the same weight of chlorine as in our first experiment we should expect that the charge passed is the same, 96,500 coulombs, and that the weight of sodium deposited is 23 grams. A check shows that this is so. We now weigh the chlorine collected at each of the anodes of the other three solutions. It should be obvious that for each this weight should be the

[9] Dissolved in molten cryolite to make it ionize.

same as that of the first beaker, i.e., 35.5 grams, for we passed the same quantity of charge through each. Next we weigh the substances collected at each of the cathodes. For beaker 2 this will be hydrogen; we find that it weighs one gram (actually 1.008 grams if there is no experimental error). We note that this weight is *numerically* equal to the atomic weight of hydrogen. It is therefore one gram atomic weight of hydrogen. The magnesium collected from beaker 3 weighs a bit over 12 grams. We note that this weight is *numerically* equal to one-half its atomic weight, and is therefore one-half a gram-atomic weight of magnesium. The aluminum collected from beaker 4 weighs about 9 grams, a weight that is *numerically* equal to one third its atomic weight and so is one-third of a gram-atomic weight of aluminum.

Immediately we ask: Why not one gram atomic weight of magnesium and aluminum? Why one gram atomic weight each of chlorine, sodium, and hydrogen and only a half or a third for the others? The answer is to be found in the differences in valence which has been defined as the combining capacity of atoms. Chlorine, sodium, and hydrogen all have a valence of one, and so are monovalent elements. Magnesium has a valence of two. This means not only that it has twice the combining capacity of chlorine, sodium, or hydrogen, but also that the positive charge on one atom of it is sufficient to neutralize the negative charges on two atoms of chlorine. Hence if a chlorine atom has one excess electron, it takes the excess electrons from two atoms of chlorine to make up the deficiency of two electrons on one magnesium atom. Therefore the number of magnesium atoms released at the cathode will be half the number of chlorine atoms released at the anode. Since an Avogadro's number [10] (6×10^{23}) of atoms of chlorine, equal to one gram atomic weight (35.5 grams), are released, only half that number (3×10^{23}) of atoms of magnesium, equal to one-half a gram atomic weight [11] (12.16 grams) are released by the same quantity of charge. The same reasoning applies to aluminum except that its valence is 3, and we need to substitute 3 for 2, one-

[10] This number was not known until some forty years after Faraday's death. The reader should understand that the reasoning given here is in light of modern knowledge. If Faraday had known this number and its significance, he undoubtedly would have reasoned as we have here.

[11] The atomic weight of magnesium is 24.32.

third for one-half, 2×10^{23} for 3×10^{23}, and 9 grams [12] for 12.16 grams in the above account.

We may summarize the observed facts in the above two experiments in Faraday's law of electrolysis, as follows:

The weight of the element released at either electrode is directly proportional to the amount of charge and to its atomic weight, but is inversely proportional to its valence.

The Smallest
Bit of Electricity

Faraday seems not to have carried his reasoning further. If he had, he undoubtedly would have reached the conclusion that there exists a particle of electricity that is the smallest possible, just as there exists a particle of elemental matter that is the smallest possible for that kind of matter; i.e., just as there are atoms of matter there are "atoms" of electricity. He would also have reached the conclusion that this smallest bit of electricity is that associated with monovalent ions. Bivalent ions carry two of these bits and trivalent ions three.

A few years after Faraday's death Johnstone Stoney came to these conclusions after reading Faraday's papers on electrolysis. Stoney named this smallest particle the *electron,* although more than twenty years were to elapse before the electron was discovered. Probably Faraday did reach these conclusions in his mind but didn't put them on paper, possibly because of doubt at the time of the value of the atomic theory, due to the failure to reconcile it with the law of combining volumes (see Chapter 6).

How does Faraday's work integrate with what we have already said about the structure of matter? First, we can no longer say, if we wish to be precise, that all matter consists of atoms or molecules, for some matter consists of ions. We will learn later that the negative ion of an element is a bit more than an atom and that a positive ion is a bit less than an atom. Faraday didn't know this.

[12] The atomic weight of aluminum is 26.98.

He did know that matter was electrical in nature and that all matter, under proper conditions, can be electrically charged. A question arises. Is this charge associated with matter in the bulk, or is it associated with the individual atoms or molecules that compose that matter? The evidence from electrolysis strongly suggests the latter. If true, then we are forced to conclude that the smallest bit of charge on any ion is that associated with ions formed from monovalent atoms, and that there are 6×10^{23} of these smallest bits of charge in 96,500 coulombs (called "one faraday of charge" henceforth; see footnote 8). The reasoning is straightforward. One faraday will release 6×10^{23} atoms of a monovalent element from an electrolytic solution. Before release these atoms were single ions in solution, 6×10^{23} of them, each lacking one of these smallest bits of charge if each ion is positively charged. The total deficiency in bits of charge was therefore 6×10^{23}. If the ions were negative and singly charged, they had a total excess of 6×10^{23} of these bits. During electrolysis these excess charges were given up at the anode, passed through the battery to the cathode to supply the 6×10^{23} positive ions with the one charge each necessary to change them into atoms. We further conclude that ions formed from bivalent atoms have either two too few or two too many bits, and that ions formed from trivalent atoms have either three too few or three too many bits. From here it is, of course, only a short step to the conclusion that one of these bits is the smallest possible amount of charge that can exist. The distribution of quantity of charge among ions of all kinds makes little sense otherwise. What we are saying here is that electricity is particulate in nature; i.e., it is composed of particles (called electrons) just as matter is composed of particles, and that in any quantity of charge there is an integral (never a fractional) number of charges. This means that there is no such thing as one-half, two-thirds, or the like, of a bit. We have already seen that Johnstone Stoney arrived at this conclusion simply from reading Faraday's work. General acceptance, however, had to await confirmation from some other source, despite the fact that the argument for it *as we have presented it to you* seems irrefutable. The fly in the ointment is that figure, 6×10^{23} (Avogadro's number), a number not determined until long after the deaths of both Faraday and Stoney. Without it, and without isolation of the charge or evidence from another source, the conviction that Stoney was right was not of much use. One could, however, speculate, using very simple algebra, as follows: Suppose we assume that the size of the charge of this smallest bit of charge is designated by e. Let us also suppose that the number of monovalent atoms released at either anode or cathode is designated by n, and the charge transported through the solution in releasing n atoms is given by Q. We then have: *charge transported = charge on one ion × number of atoms deposited*. In symbols

$$Q = en$$

Now let M represent the total mass deposited and m the mass of a single atom of the element released. Then mass deposited = mass of one atom × number of atoms deposited. In symbols

$$M = mn.$$

Dividing one equation by the other [13]

$$\frac{Q = en}{M = mn} \quad \text{or} \quad \frac{Q}{M} = \frac{en}{mn}$$

Since n cancels out,

$$\frac{Q}{M} = \frac{e}{m}$$

In words

$$\frac{\text{charge transported}}{\text{mass deposited}} = \frac{\text{charge on each ion}}{\text{mass of one atom}}$$

Q and M can be measured, Q by measuring the current (with an ammeter) and the time during which it is flowing, M by weighing the amount of the element released. This gives us e/m (to be read e over m). If we knew either e or m, we could calculate the other.

Even if we had a way of measuring e/m without knowing either e or m, experimentally, we would feel confident that our reasoning from the facts of electrolysis was sound. Eventually this was done—but let us not get too far ahead of our story. If we know Avogadro's number and its meaning, we can determine n in $Q = en$, for Q is then 96,500 coulombs. Thus $96,500 = e \times 6 \times 10^{23}$.

[13] Dividing one equation by another is a simple easily provable mathematical device for simplifying and making more readily apparent relationships that might otherwise not be suspected.

Transposing

$$e = \frac{96,500}{6 \times 10^{23}} = \frac{9.65 \times 10^4}{6 \times 10^{23}} = 1.6 \times 10^{-19} \text{ coulomb/electron}$$

(Compare with footnote 9 of this chapter.) But, as we have already stated, Avogadro's number was not known in either Faraday's or Stoney's time.

It will undoubtedly be helpful to summarize the contents of this chapter. Electrolytes are compounds which in either the molten state or in water solution will carry an electric current. In electrolytic solutions or in liquids composed of molten electrolytes there is a motion during electrolysis of charged particles (ions) towards one or the other of the two electrodes. Metallic ions, and those of hydrogen, migrate to the negative electrode (cathode) and so must carry at least one positive charge. Nonmetallic ions (other than hydrogen) migrate to the positive electrode (anode) and so must carry at least one negative charge. Ions become neutral atoms when they reach an electrode, positive ions by gaining charges and negative ions by losing charges. Faraday's Law of Electrolysis (sometimes broken up into two laws) states that the same amount of charge will deposit or liberate different weights of different elements, and that the weight deposited or liberated is directly proportional to the atomic weight of the element and inversely proportional to the valence. This law, like all laws, rests directly on experiment or observation. From this law Johnstone Stoney reasoned that a monovalent ion carries a single indivisible charge that he called an electron; bivalent ions carry two and trivalent ions three electrons. Thus the work of Faraday led to a concept of matter in a new form (ions); it also related charge to atomic weight and valence, and in doing so indicated an intimate relationship between electricity and chemistry. We will understand this relationship better when we get around to answering the question "Where and how did these ions get their charges originally?"

CHAPTER 11

Evidences for the Divisibility of the Atom

The Discovery of the Electron

We have already stated that the invention of the battery led to the investigation of the passage of an electric current through liquid solutions. It also led to the investigation of the passage of a current through gases, an investigation which was delayed a few decades because of the difficulties involved. Gases at atmospheric pressures are excellent insulators, and so high voltages [1] are needed, voltages unobtainable from batteries until one of the electrical discoveries of Faraday made possible the invention of the induction coil.[2] It was early discovered that much lower voltages could be used if most of the gas was pumped out of a receptacle equipped with two sealed-in electrodes—usually in a glass tube such as that shown in Fig. 7—which was then sealed to maintain the low gas pressure. Such a tube is called a gas discharge tube. Familiar examples are the tubes used for fluorescent lighting and in neon lighting for ad-

[1] High voltage in the flow of electricity corresponds to high pressure in the flow of water through the pipes supplying water to our houses. The scientist commonly uses the words *potential difference* in place of *voltage,* words which refer to the difference in electrical potential energy between two electrodes.

[2] The induction coil rather than the simple transformer is used in these experiments because direct current is necessary. Simple transformers work only with alternating current. The induction coil is essentially a simple transformer that is provided with an interrupter to break the current rapidly in the primary coil (of the transformer).

vertising. In such tubes the current is carried from the cathode to the anode by charged particles just as in electrolytic solutions. Our problem is the investigation of the nature of these charged particles.

A few ions, created in more than one way, are always present in any gas. Some result from collisions between the gas molecules, and some from collisions with cosmic rays from outer space or with naturally radioactive particles that are always present. A positive ion is formed if one or more charges are torn loose from a molecule of the gas in one of these collisions. These charges quickly attach themselves to other molecules of the gas, forming negative ions. Once formed, these ions of opposite charge attract one another. If two collide, both ions may be neutralized by a transfer of the excess charge from the negative to the positive ion. We will call this process "recombination." When the number of ions present is relatively small, there is little recombination because the likelihood of a collision between two oppositely charged ions is small. Increase of the rate of ion formation results in a greater rate of increase in recombination since the likelihood of collision has increased. For any particular set of conditions an equilibrium is soon reached between ion formation and ion recombination; i.e., as many ions are recombined as there are ions formed.

The use of a vacuum pump decreases the number of gas mole-

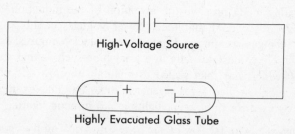

High-Voltage Source

Highly Evacuated Glass Tube

FIG. 7. *Simple Gas Discharge Tube.* If the tube is highly evacuated and the voltage high enough, the current will flow from one electrode to the other. The high voltage source must provide direct current. In the early stages of evacuation, the current is carried by ions of whatever gas is in the tube. In the later stages, after the pressure has become extremely low, it is carried by cathode rays (later identified as electrons).

cules in the discharge tube, reducing the chances of collisions [3] between either molecules or ions. The equilibrium is upset by this reduction, but for any fixed pressure of the gas a new equilibrium is attained if all other conditions remain constant. A high voltage applied to the electrodes also upsets the equilibrium by changing the rate of ion formation. Some neutral gas molecules come in contact with one or the other of the highly charged electrodes, gaining a charge from the cathode or losing one to the anode, creating new ions. If the newly created ion is positive, it is accelerated [4] away from the anode and toward the cathode; if negative, it is accelerated away from the cathode and toward the anode. Those reaching the cathode gain charges, and those reaching the anode lose charges. This is exactly what happens in the passage of current through an electrolytic solution, and so we might expect that this is the way the current is carried through gases.

There is one flaw in the above reasoning. If we use gases at atmospheric pressure, no current is recorded even by extremely delicate detecting devices unless the voltage is extremely high. If, however, we reduce the gas pressure in the tube by a vacuum pump, we increase the distances between gas molecules, reduce the number of collisions, and increase the speeds of the accelerated ions because they can travel greater distances between collisions. The net result is that a greater number of ions reach the electrode to which they are attracted. If the pressure is sufficiently reduced, the current is considerable even with only a moderately high voltage. Thus there is a two-way migration of the ions—positive ones toward the cathode, negative ones toward the anode—just as is the case of electrolytic solutions.

If the gas pressure within the discharge tube is of the order of 1/760 that of atmospheric pressure, equivalent to 1 millimeter of mercury, the passage of the current, detectable by an ammeter in the circuit, is made visible because the gas begins to glow with light of a color dependent on the particular gas in the tube. This is the light we see in fluorescent and neon tubes. If still more air is

[3] The number of collisions made by a molecule of a gas with other molecules of the gas at normal atmospheric pressure and 0° C. is of the order of five billion per second.

[4] Acceleration is defined as the *time rate of increase in velocity*. We accelerate a car when we increase or decrease its speed. The acceleration is positive if the speed is increased, negative if decreased.

removed,[5] the glow slowly becomes fainter until it ceases entirely. A glance at the ammeter shows no detectable current. The only explanation is that evacuation of the tube has reached the stage where there are not enough ions to carry a detectable current.

If we continue the evacuation [6] there shortly appears another glow, this time a green one regardless of the kind of gas in the tube. It appears to emanate from the inside walls of the glass tube. A check of the ammeter shows that a current is again flowing. Apparently something other than ions of the gas is carrying the current. This unknown "something" was given the name "cathode rays" because simple tests showed that they came from the cathode.

The nature of these rays [7] was the subject of many investigations in the 1880's. Now it was already known that a current-carrying wire, free to move, will be thrust sideways if placed in a magnetic field,[8] e.g., between the poles of a horseshoe magnet. If a beam of cathode rays constitute an electric current, then it should show a similar deflection. Experimentation (Fig. 10) shows that it

[5] Progress in these investigations was slow because vacuum pumps of the times were not good enough to evacuate tubes to the necessary low pressures. This is an excellent example of a case where scientific investigation had to await advances in technology, advances which commonly spring from economic considerations. This was true of the vacuum pump, for Edison's invention of the electric light bulb resulted in a demand for efficient means of producing evacuated bulbs.

[6] The gas pressure in modern discharge tubes of this sort is about a millionth of an atmosphere. This is about a billion times *greater* than the best vacuum now obtainable.

[7] A ray, or beam of rays, may consist of a stream of particles, charged or uncharged, or it may be a stream of light waves, or of waves akin to those of light, e.g., ultraviolet waves. Cathode rays are obviously not rays of visible light for they are themselves invisible (the green glow described above is an effect produced by the rays striking the glass tube.)

[8] A magnetic field surrounds every magnetic pole (Fig. 8). This field is an alteration of the space about the pole, an alteration that can be detected in either of two ways. The simplest is to bring another magnetic pole into that space. If the strengh of the field is great enough, obvious attraction or repulsion will take place. The other, much more difficult in practice, is to bring a *moving* charge into that space. The moving charge will neither be attracted nor repelled, but instead will be deflected from its straight-line path in a direction that is in *every* case at right angles to both the straight-line path and the direction of the field (Fig. 9). The deflection is thus a sideway thrust. The direction of the field is said to be from the north pole of a magnet to the south pole. That the field has direction can be shown by reversing the poles of the magnet, whereupon the deflection of the moving charge will also be reversed—though it is still a sideway thrust. This sideway thrust is the principle that makes the electric motor possible.

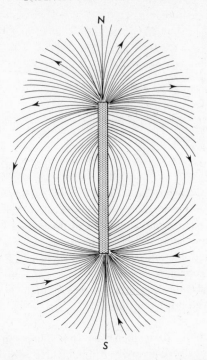

FIG. 8. *Magnetic Field.* Lines of force about a bar magnet. The orientation of the field is indicated by arrows on the lines of force. Note that they are directed outward from the north pole and inward toward the south pole.

does. This is strong evidence (but not final proof) that the cathode rays are beams of charged particles, for no known beams of rays akin to light showed any evidence of deflection. Moreover, the direction of the deflection was shown always to be in the direction that negatively charged particles are deflected. This clinched the argument about the charge of the rays. Now if the rays are particles, then the particles should have mass (hereafter designated by m). Each particle should presumably also show a fixed quantity of negative charge (hereafter designated by e). No investigator succeeded in measuring either e or m at the time, but several did determine the ratio of e to m, commonly written e/m, and read as "e over m."

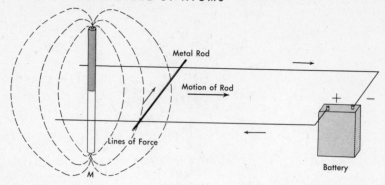

FIG. 9. *Current-Carrying Copper Rod in a Magnetic Field.* The copper rod, free to move, lies in contact with bare wires. When the magnet, M, is absent the rod remains stationary as the current flows. When the magnet is brought near, the rod is thrust sideway. If the magnet is turned end for end, the thrust will also be sideway but in the opposite direction. Since copper is nonmagnetic, it is apparent that the thrust is not caused by magnetic attraction or repulsion. It is this sideway thrust that makes electric motors possible.

Foremost among these men was J. J. Thomson, Professor of Physics at Cambridge University, England. He is given credit over other men because his investigations were more detailed and broader in scope than theirs. The proof that the particles were negatively charged was easy. All that was necessary was to show that they behaved like negatively charged ions rather than like positively charged ones. But were they ions? The solution of this problem was to subject them to measurements of some sort. As already indicated, it was known that moving charged particles are deflected when they pass through a magnetic field. Measurement of the amount of this deflection does not in itself help, for the magnitude of the force which determines the amount of deflection for a particle of a particular mass m depends not only on the amount of charge carried but also on the velocity of the particle and the strength of the magnetic field; i.e., Force (F) = magnetic field strength (H) × charge (e) × velocity (v). Symbolically, $F = Hev$. What we would like to know here is the value of e, the charge on a particular particle of mass m. H is easily calculated by use of an electromagnet of known strength; however, F and v are also un-

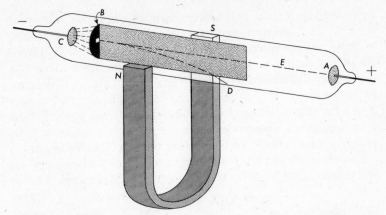

FIG. 10. *Deflection of Cathode Rays (Electrons) in a Magnetic Field.* High voltage source not shown. C, cathode; A, anode; B, plate with a hole in it to provide a narrow beam of rays; E, undeflected beam when the magnet is absent; D, deflected beam when the magnet is present. Note that the deflection is downward, i.e., at right angles to both the direction of the magnetic field (N to S) and to the direction of motion of the rays. If the poles of the magnet are reversed, thereby reversing the magnetic field, the deflection of the rays will be upward.

known. No single equation can be solved if there is more than one unknown; here we have three, *F, e,* and *v.* Thomson's problem was to reduce the number of unknowns.

First, he took advantage of the fact that charged particles are also deflected in moving through an electric field.[9] A moving negative charge will be deflected toward the positively charged plate. Now it can be shown that the force acting on any beam of cathode rays passing through an electric field (and hence deflecting the beam) depends upon the strength of the electric field and the amount of charge carried by the cathode rays; i.e., force $(F) =$ electric field strength $(E) \times$ charge (e). Symbolically, $F = Ee$.

If now we pass a cathode ray through a magnetic field and an electric field at the same time, there will be two forces acting

[9] Just as there is a magnetic field about every magnetic pole, there is an electric field about every electric charge. If we attach two parallel metal plates to the poles of a battery (Fig. 11), an electric field is created between the plates. One plate will be positively charged, the other negatively.

simultaneously on the ray. Moreover, if we orient our equipment correctly, the two forces can be made to oppose each other. For example, we can place the plates governing our electric field horizontally with the positively charged plate lowermost. Thus the moving ray will tend to be deflected downward (Fig. 11). We then place our magnet so that its magnetic field will be oriented in such a way that the moving ray will tend to be deflected upward. Now if we regulate the magnitudes of the electric and the magnetic fields properly, we can make the beam move through these fields with no deflection at all; i.e., the force tending to deflect the beam upward will exactly equal the force tending to deflect it downward. Thus

$$Hev = Ee \text{ [10]}$$

[10] We have $F = Hev$ and $F = Ee$. Since the F in one equation is equal to the F in the other, $Hev = Ee$.

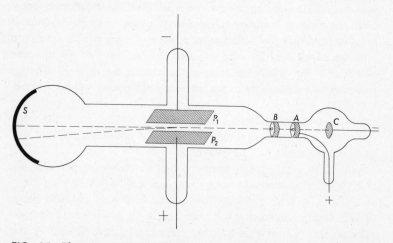

FIG. 11. *Thomson's Apparatus for His Determination of e/m (Somewhat Modernized).* High voltage source not shown. C, cathode; A, anode with a hole in it; B, plate with a hole in it to provide a narrow beam of rays; P_1 and P_2, plates charged by an electric current so as to deflect the rays downward (by electrostatic attractions); S, a fluorescent screen to make the rays "visible." Not shown is the electromagnet whose magnetic field lies at right angles to the plane of the paper and oriented so as to deflect the rays upward. If the downward and the upward deflecting forces are equal, there is no deflection.

Since e occurs on both sides of the equation, we can cancel it out. So, $Hv = E$. Dividing both sides by H, we have

$$v = \frac{E}{H}$$

Now the value of both E and H can be determined, E by placing a voltmeter in the circuit with the charged plates, and H by using an electromagnet of known strength. Thus v, the velocity of the ray, can be calculated. For the particular equipment that Thomson used, this turned out to be about 10,000 miles per second. This determination reduced the unknowns mentioned in the equation $F = Hev$ to two, e and F.

More than two hundred years earlier Newton, in his work on the laws of motion, had determined that the force F, acting on a body moving in a circle at uniform speed, is given by $F = mv^2/r$, where m is the mass of the body, v its velocity, and r is the radius of the circle in which the body is moving. Now if we deflect a charged particle in a *large* electric field of *uniform strength,* the deflection will be uniform and continuous in that field. In other words, its path in that field will be an arc of a circle (Fig. 40), and the above equation for uniform circular motion will apply. Hence we have

$$F = Hev \qquad \text{and} \qquad F = \frac{mv^2}{r}$$

Since things equal to the same thing are equal to each other,

$$Hev = \frac{mv^2}{r}$$

Dividing each side of the equation by Hvm, we have

$$\frac{e}{m} = \frac{v}{Hr}$$

Since all terms on the right are known (v is 10,000 mi/sec, H can be determined if an electromagnet is used, and r can be measured directly), the ratio of e/m can be calculated. This ratio of charge to mass of the charged particles constituting cathode rays turned out to be 1.76×10^8 coulombs per gram of particles. This means that 1 gram of these particles moving through a wire (or system of wires) will furnish 176,000,000 coulombs of electricity, enough to keep a 100-watt light bulb burning 24 hours a day for nearly 6 years. (A nickel weighs about 5 grams.)

Thomson had to be content with this ratio for he could conceive of no way of measuring either e or m. By using many different metals as his cathodes and obtaining cathode rays with the same e/m ratio from them all, he was able to prove conclusively that these rays were universal constituents of all matter. Cathode rays soon came to be known as "electrons," the name that Stoney (p. 65) gave to the charge on monovalent ions and which he considered to be the smallest bit of electricity possible. Thomson was at first reluctant to advance the idea that atoms were not the indivisible particles envisaged by Dalton, but are instead complex mechanical systems composed of positively and negatively charged parts. Only his repeated experiments convinced him that there was no escape from the conclusion that cathode rays (electrons) were particles far lighter than atoms.

How large are these particles? To find out let us turn their e/m ratio upside down so that it reads m/e. Using the same figures that gave us 1.76×10^8 coulombs per gram, but inverting them and using the faraday for our unit of charge instead of the coulomb (96,500 coulombs = 1 faraday), we find that this m/e ratio is equal to about 0.00055 gram per faraday. This means that if Thomson had continued his experiment until 96,500 coulombs (1 faraday) had passed through the circuit, the total weight of the electrons emitted from the cathode would have been 0.00055 gram. You will recall (Chapter 10) that Faraday in his electrolysis experiment would have collected 1.008 gram of hydrogen atoms (the lightest of all atoms) at the anode if he had passed an equivalent amount of charge (96,500 coulombs) through an HCl solution. The ratio of the weight of the hydrogen atom to the weight of the electron is therefore 1.008/0.00055 or 1,833. This means that it takes 1,833 electrons to equal the weight of 1 hydrogen atom.

At first Thomson had few converts, for the concept of the indivisible atom was deeply rooted. More evidence was needed. Could the concept that electrons were parts of all atoms, parts that could be detached from them or added to others, explain other phenomena that heretofore had gone unexplained? If it could do so for one or two such phenomena, then some doubts about the concept could be removed; and if enough phenomena are explained by it, especially if they were of a sort very different from that which originally gave rise to the concept, all doubts would be removed. Let us consider ions first, assuming, of course, that Thomson was right in saying that electrons are universal constituents of all matter. We have referred to ions as charged atoms; atoms which have at least one more or one less charge than neutral atoms. The term "charge" is a nondescript one. When we say that an atom has gained or lost a charge we are not really stating what it has lost or gained. If we substitute electron for charge, we are being much more definitive, for an electron is a definite particle with a specific mass and quantity of charge. Since atoms of every kind contain electrons, each with a single negative charge, ions are simply atoms that have either too many or too few electrons. An ion can be deflected in magnetic and electric fields, and the ratio of its charge to its mass can be determined in exactly the same way as that used in determining e/m for the electron. In the electrolysis of molten sodium chloride, we raised the question about the origin of the positive sodium and the negative chlorine ions. The question is answered if we assume that each chlorine atom has taken one electron away from each sodium atom.[11] The phenomena concerning ions in a gas discharge tube are also explainable by the electron concept. A positively charged ion is formed when one or more electrons are torn loose from a neutral atom, negatively charged ones when one or more of these now free electrons become attached to a neutral atom. Thus, the electron concept helps us to explain ions and their behavior.

Another phenomenon had gone unexplained since Thomas Edison had first observed it in 1883. Why, in Fig. 12, does a current flow in the ammeter (galvanometer) even though the plate, P, is not connected to F to complete a circuit? Why does it flow only when the bulb filament F is red hot? Why does it *fail* to flow if the plate is connected to the negative side of the circuit, thereby putting a negative charge on the plate? The electron concept easily answers these questions. Electrons are ejected from a hot filament, and the hotter the filament the greater the number ejected, a process somewhat similar to the evaporation of a liquid. The ejected electrons, carrying a negative charge, are attracted to the plate when

[11] A further insight into this phenomenon is given in Chapter 18.

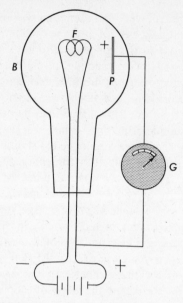

FIG. 12. *Thermionic Emission of Electrons (Edison Effect)*. P is a metal plate inserted in an ordinary electric light bulb, B. The plate is connected to the positive side of the circuit that lights the bulb via the galvanometer, G. The plate is therefore positively charged. Note that this circuit is apparently not complete, for there is no visible connection between P and F. Yet a current flows as soon as F gets hot. Electrons are ejected from the hot filament, F, by the heat, and attracted to P, thereby completing the circuit.

it is positively charged, and so move toward it across the space from *F* to *P*. This movement constitutes the current. The reason no current flows when the plate is negatively charged should be obvious [12] if one remembers that electrons are negatively charged; the plate repels the electrons so that there is no circuit.

[12] Edison put such a plate in a bulb when he was trying to improve electric light bulbs. He noted the foregoing facts about the flow of the current but did not further investigate the phenomenon, for he could see no way in which it would help him improve the bulb. If he had investigated it, he would have discovered the principle of the radio tube. All radio and TV tubes are simply variations of the above bulb. The wait between the turning on of a radio or a TV set is necessitated by the need of the filament to get hot before electrons can be ejected from them.

An electric current is easily explained by the electron concept. According to it, a current is simply a flow of electrons through a conductor, e.g., a copper wire. The electrons, or some of them at least, present in the copper atoms move back and forth in the wire to produce alternating current,[13] or continuously in one direction through the wire in direct current. The difference between conductors and insulators also can be deduced from the electron concept. Conductors are substances whose atoms hold their electrons (or some of them at least) loosely, so that they can move about with comparatively little "urging," whereas the atoms of insulators hold all of their electrons more closely. Since metals are all good conductors and nonmetals are all good insulators (there are no perfect conductors and no perfect insulators), we have here one important distinction between a metal and a nonmetal. Since heat is molecular motion (Chapter 7) and the higher the temperature the greater this motion, raising the temperature of a metal increases the kinetic energy of the electrons. If the temperature is high enough, some of the electrons gain enough energy to escape from the metal just as molecules do from an evaporating liquid. Thus, the reason for thermionic emission of electrons (Fig. 12) from a hot cathode is explained.

The electron concept also explains why the current flows in the photoelectric effect (pp.129–131). It also opened up a possible explanation of atomic spectra, a subject that is dealt with in some detail in Chapter 15. Moreover, the electron concept was later found to aid explanations of most chemical reactions greatly (Chapter 18). Today electrons are considered to be as real as the atoms of which they are a part.

[13] The impetus that is the cause of the alternating motion of the electrons is a continuously changing magnetic field brought about by the electric generator (dynamo) in the powerhouse. Direct current is furnished by batteries in which chemical action induces the electrons to move. Direct current can also be derived from alternating current by a device like that shown in Fig. 12, or it can be generated by a direct current generator. Note that if the current flowing through the main circuit is alternating, the plate is alternately positively and negatively charged. Electrons flow from F to P (never from P to F) only when P is positively charged. Thus the current through the circuit which includes the galvanometer is direct current.

The Discovery of Radioactivity

A very different phenomenon which had great influence in convincing scientists that the atom was divisible was observed at almost the same time that Thomson performed his e/m experiments. It was known that certain minerals glowed (fluoresced) in the dark. Henri Becquerel of France was investigating these minerals to see if they emitted X rays—which had been discovered a few months earlier. He found that all minerals containing either uranium or thorium continuously emitted a radiation that fogged well-wrapped, unexposed photographic plates even in complete darkness, and that they did so spontaneously; i.e., there was nothing that man could do to stop it, slow it down, or speed it up. The term "radioactive" was applied to elements, minerals, or other compounds that emitted such radiations. Becquerel also discovered that uranium and thorium could not account for all of the emitted radiation from the minerals responsible for the fogging. He turned the problem over to one of his student assistants, Marie Curie. She, together with her husband, eventually discovered the new elements radium and polonium, both highly radioactive.

The problem remained to identify the radations emitted. First, were they particles or waves? The problem was solved in the same way as for the identification of cathode rays; they were passed through electric and magnetic fields (Fig. 13). The result was that three distinct types of radiations were found. For want of better names at the time they were called "alpha," "beta," and "gamma" rays (the first three letters of the Greek alphabet). In time the beta rays were found to carry a single negative charge, to have the same e/m ratio as electrons, and to behave otherwise as electrons. Beta rays are therefore electrons, but electrons which have a far higher velocity than any obtained from cathodes in gas discharge tubes (Fig. 7). Alpha particles were found to carry a double positive charge, and to be deflected far less in a magnetic field than were the beta rays (electrons; see Fig. 13). This suggested that their charge was small in comparison with their masses. Comparison of their e/m ratio with that of hydrogen ions suggested that they were

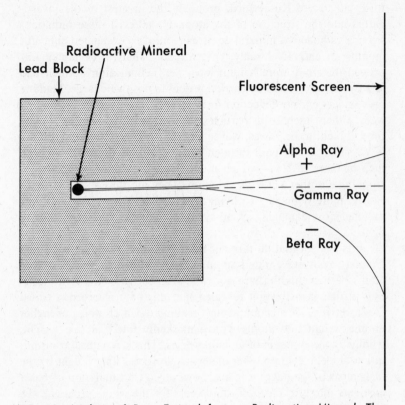

FIG. 13. *Analysis of Rays Emitted from a Radioactive Mineral.* The lead block absorbs all rays except those traveling toward the screen. The rays pass through an electric field (not shown) on their way to the screen. They are deflected as shown. If a magnetic field is substituted for the electric field, the alpha and the beta rays will also be deflected, but the gamma rays still remain unaffected. Thus alpha and beta rays are proved to be streams of charged particles, and gamma rays to be either waves or uncharged particles. Further analysis proves them to be waves.

helium [14] ions. Proof that they were was obtained by Ernest Rutherford, later Lord Rutherford, probably the greatest of the investigators into the structure of the atom. He allowed these radiations
from a radioactive mineral to stream into an evacuated tube for
months on end. Eventually, spectroscopic analysis (Chapter 15)
proved that they were helium ions, i.e., helium atoms which had
lost two electrons and so carried a double positive charge. Gamma
rays underwent no deflection in electric or magnetic fields, and so
were either uncharged particles or waves. Investigation finally
proved them to be waves, waves akin to those of visible light. Like
X rays they could pass through opaque objects, even through an
inch or more of lead—which is an element extremely effective in
stopping all other kinds of radiation. They are thus a sort of super
X ray, more damaging to living tissues than X rays; in fact, they
are the most damaging of all types of radiation that are akin to
light.

It is evident that all three of these radiations—alpha, beta, and
gamma rays—are emitted spontaneously with high energies from
atoms of elements that are above lead in the atomic weight scale.
Still further investigation revealed that this natural process, called
"radioactivity," is a spontaneous breaking down of atoms of higher
atomic weight into atoms with a markedly lower atomic weight,
wholly by the emission of alpha particles. This is a natural transmutation of elements into other elements, a process long sought by the
alchemists of long ago; it is not, however, a transmutation of baser
elements into gold. It took some years for the whole process to be
understood; when it was, there could no longer be any doubt about
the divisibility of the atom.

[14] Helium, chemical symbol He, is the second lightest of the elements;
its ions have four times the mass of hydrogen ions. Doubly charged helium
ions are still called alpha particles. They played a great part in the unraveling of the structure of the atom. The reader should therefore clearly
understand what they are.

Measuring the Charge on the Electron

Even before the final conclusions were drawn concerning radioactive processes, an American physicist, Robert Millikan, measured the charge on the electron by means of an ingenuous experiment. Even though the experiment was simple, we will not attempt to describe it here. Suffice it to say that after hundreds of patient observations, he determined the charge on the electron to be 1.6×10^{-19} coulombe. This means that it takes the charge on about 6 billion billion electrons to equal 1 coulomb—which is the amount of electricity that passes through a lighted 100-watt bulb each second. Hence the charge on the electron is extremely small.

Once e, the charge on the electron, had been computed, m, the mass of the electron, could be computed from the e/m ratio as determined by J. J. Thomson, as follows:

$$e/m = 1.76 \times 10^8 \text{ coulombs/gm}$$

Multiplying both sides of the equation by m, we have

$$e = 1.76 \times 10^8 \times m$$

Dividing both sides by 1.76×10^8, we have

$$\frac{e}{1.76 \times 10^8} = m$$

Substituting 1.6×10^{-19} for e

$$\frac{1.6 \times 10^{-19} \text{ coulomb}}{1.76 \times 10^8 \text{ coulombs/gm}} = m = 9.1 \times 10^{-28} \text{ gm}$$

In decimals,

9.1×10^{-28} gram is 0.00000000000000000000000000091 gm.

A gram, you will remember, is about two-fifths the weight of a new dime. Thus it takes over 22 billion billion billion electrons to weigh as much as a dime. We have shown that the charge on the electron is extremely small, but so is the mass of the electron. *Relative* to its mass, the charge on the electron is enormous, for the total charge on enough electrons to weigh as much as a dime is sufficient to keep a 100-watt bulb burning 24 hours per day for nearly 15 years.

CHAPTER 12

Rutherford's Nuclear
Theory of the Atom

That an atom had so definite a structure that scientists could confidently refer to different parts of it had now become certain. Electrons with their negative charges had been proved to be universal constituents of all matter; the existence of positive ions, commonly called positive rays in this context, carrying positive electricity had been demonstrated; and alpha particles had been proved to be ejected from certain kinds of heavy atoms during the process of natural radioactive decomposition. Attention naturally turned to what the rest of the atom consisted of and to the number and arrangement of the electrons.

Various theories about the latter were advanced, none of them based on crucial experiments of any kind, so we will not review them here, except to state that one of them assumed the electrons to be scattered through the atom like seeds in a watermelon. One of the problems was the vastly greater amount of matter associated with the positive rays compared to that associated with the electrons. The belief was general, however, that all atoms contained positively charged hydrogen [1] ions which are now called "protons" (meaning primary). This concept was first advanced by William Prout, a British chemist, about 1817. He made the suggestion that hydrogen was the primordial substance out of which all other atoms were made. His evidence was that atomic weights of many elements as then known were almost even multiples of that of the hydrogen

[1] Hydrogen is the lightest and smallest of all atoms.

atom. The idea was abandoned as more careful atomic weight determinations showed that many were not. We will see later how right Prout was, although in a way that would have astounded him.

It was not long before scientists were "firing" electrons at other atoms to see if other parts could be knocked loose from them. They failed because the electron was too light and too small. It penetrated matter, but that was all. Attention turned to the alpha particle which weighed about 7,500 times as much as the electron, and so was therefore far more effective as an atomic "bullet." It turned out to be the first really effective disrupter of other atoms.

The alpha particle owed its effectiveness not only to its mass but also to the fact that it was ejected from radioactive atoms with velocities of about 10,000 miles per second, and so had an enormous kinetic energy. As previously stated, it could knock electrons loose from gas atoms. At the time, no way was known to see what actually happened to the alpha particles as they traveled through the gas. However, fired at a screen coated with zinc sulphide to make it fluoresce, their individual effect can be seen easily if a low-power microscope is used in a completely darkened room, for each particle produces a tiny flash of light on hitting the screen. By varying the distance of the screen from the source of the particles, their range could be determined. The rather amazing discovery was soon made that if a very thin metal foil is placed between the source and the screen, most of the particles pass through the foil as if it were not there, i.e. there is no loss of kinetic energy. A few alpha particles are slowed down, and some are deflected from their paths by varying amounts. All are stopped, however, by slightly thicker foils.

Rutherford decided to use a gold foil in his experiments, for it is the most malleable substance known; it can be hammered out, without tearing, into sheets so thin that a pile of over 250,000 sheets is only an inch thick. Nevertheless, each sheet is still several thousands of atoms thick. For his source of alpha particles, he used a speck of radium. By use of the apparatus shown in Fig. 14 he was able to obtain a thin pencil of particles. At first these were allowed to impinge directly on the screen. All of the hits were within a small circle whose diameter was approximately that of the beam.

The gold foil was then placed directly in the path of the beam. Most of the alpha particles went through without deviation, producing flashes on the screen. Many, however, were deflected by small amounts, so that the spot on the screen that included most of the "hits" had a diameter somewhat greater than that which was made by the thin pencil of alpha particles when the gold foil was absent. Some flashes were, however, observed on the screen far out from this central spot. Thus, on passing through the gold foil the particles are scattered somewhat (Figs. 14–15), so this experiment is sometimes referred to as Rutherford's scattering of alpha particles experiment. Since some particles were very surprisingly deflected to the edge of the screen, and possibly beyond, screens were placed in a circle about the gold foil in an effort to determine the maximum angle of scattering. A few were found to be deflected 180°; i.e., they seemed to have hit something head-on so that they bounced right back in the direction from which they came (Fig. 15).

Rutherford could not interpret these results by any watermelon or plum-pudding model of the atom. Three inferences could be made from the observations. The first was that most of the atom appeared to be empty space, because most of the alpha particles went straight through the foil undeflected. The second was that those

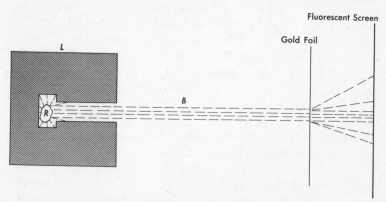

FIG. 14. *Rutherford's Gold Foil Experiment*. The apparatus is much like that in Fig. 13, except for the presence of the gold foil. The beam, *B*, consists of alpha particles radioactively ejected from *R*. Note how some are deflected from a straight-line path after passing through the foil, whereas the great majority go straight through. In the actual experiment the gold foil could be moved completely around the foil.

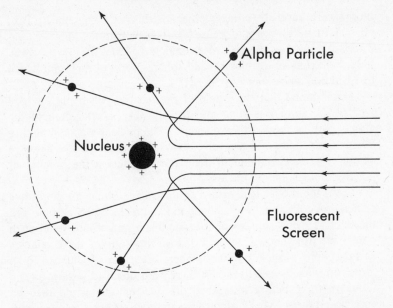

FIG. 15. *Rutherford's Gold Foil Experiment.* Alpha particles approaching an atomic nucleus. The alpha particles are scattered somewhat by the repulsive forces of the similarly charged nucleus. Those that approach closest to the nucleus are deflected the most, some almost reversing their paths. Since most go straight through or are only slightly deflected, the nuclei must be relatively far apart. Since most of the mass of the atom is concentrated in the nucleus, the atom must be mostly empty space.

particles that had been deflected through angles that ranged from small to relatively large had approached close enough to a concentration of positive charges to be turned away from it. The third was that a very few seemed to strike this concentration "head-on."

These inferences meant that the positive charges could not be scattered throughout the whole volume of the atom, for if they were, the maximum angle of deflection would be only a few degrees. The reason is that if the positive charges were scattered throughout the atom, no one alpha particle would "feel" the repulsive effect of more than a few positive charges. Striking these few head-on could not cause the alpha particle to rebound any more than a baseball (a heavy object) striking a tennis ball (a light object) in mid-air would cause the baseball to rebound. Therefore Rutherford proposed a new model, a model that swept away the last vestiges of the classic solid-sphere model of the atom which had endured since Dalton (ca. 1810).

He assumed that the whole of the massive positively charged part of the atom was concentrated in a very small region of the atom which he termed the "nucleus." The nucleus was assumed to be surrounded by a swarm of electrons, each carrying a negative charge. The total number of the electrons equaled the number of positive charges on the nucleus.

From the model Rutherford could calculate that no direct hits or head-on collisions were actually made, for the alpha particle and the nucleus carry charges of the same sign and would repel each other. We now know that gold has seventy-nine of these charges and the alpha particle only two. Therefore a particle headed for a direct hit with a nucleus would be slowed down to a stop by the repulsive force before it reached the nucleus and would then be accelerated directly back along the same path. Others whose paths would carry them to the edge of a nucleus would be deflected through smaller angles ranging from less than 180° down to near 0°. Since most particles were not deflected at all, the distances between the nuclei must be very large, relatively. The mass of an electron in any atom was considered much too small to cause any deflection of the alpha particles.

Using foils made of atoms with fewer charges on the nucleus, e.g., aluminum, it was found that the average angle of scattering was smaller than that for gold. This is acceptable according to the theory, for the smaller the total charge, the smaller is the repulsive force on the particle and the smaller any deflection. The theory seemed to be standing up under repeated testing.

By the use of rigorous mathematics and certain well-established natural laws not discussed in this book, Rutherford could also make certain estimates concerning the total positive charge on the nuclei of various kinds of atoms. This was done by comparing the scattering in different materials by alpha particles emitted from the same source. The same source was necessary to insure the same average kinetic energy for the alpha particles. At first, these estimates were crude, but they did indicate that the total number of charges on the nucleus was about equal to half the number representing the atomic weight. His first estimate for gold was about 100, the actual number being 79.

Rutherford was also able to estimate the number of charges from other factors, e.g., the thickness of the foil, the actual percentage of particles that were deflected through various angles, etc. Other calculations showed the diameter of the nucleus to be about one ten-thousandth the diameter of the atom, and the volume of the nucleus to be about one-millionth of a millionth the volume of the atom. His results showed that the diameter of an average atom is of the order 0.00000002 centimeters (2×10^{-8} cm; 0.000000008 in.) and that of the nucleus is of the order of 10^{-13} centimeters (0.000000000000025 in.).

There remained the problem of the distribution of the electrons about the nucleus. Rutherford adopted the suggestion of a Japanese physicist that the electrons revolved about the nucleus, forming a miniature planetary system. The revolving was necessary to explain why the electrons did not "fall" into the nucleus, just as the earth would fall into the sun if it stopped revolving.

Several problems immediately arose. How could a large number of the positive charges be held together in so small a nucleus against their repulsive forces? How can solid bodies be rigid in the presence of these forces? Another had to do with revolution of the electrons about the nucleus. An electron is a charge and it is being accelerated [2] as it revolves about the nucleus. According to Maxwell's electromagnetic theory (Chapter 14), an accelerated charge should radiate "light," losing energy as it does so. As it loses energy, it should move closer to the nucleus, gradually spiraling down into the nucleus. It is obvious that under average conditions the electron does none of these things; if it did, all electrons would have long since spiraled into the nucleus and there would be no such thing as light. Despite these difficulties the nuclear theory was soon widely accepted, for Rutherford's interpretations could not be disputed. The difficulties would have to await some other explanation.

[2] Acceleration is defined as the rate of change in velocity. Since velocity (in science) is defined as speed *in a given direction*, a change in direction even at uniform speed is just as much an acceleration as a change in speed is. This concept of acceleration is important in the pages which follow.

CHAPTER 13

Light as a Wave Motion

That the attainment of our present concept of the structure of atoms would depend upon an inquiry into the nature of light would have seemed as fantastic to all of the scientists of the early nineteenth century and even to most of those of the latter part of that century as it does to you. Probably more than anything else man takes light for granted, rarely asking how light originates, how light from even the nearest star, our sun, can travel the 93 million miles through space, let alone the million billion or the million trillion miles, or even more, from countless numbers of stars. Here we will answer that question as best we can. Figuratively, we will follow a beam of light down into the heart of the atom to see how such a beam originates.

One of the difficulties in writing a book such as this is the interlocking nature of so many widely different phenomena in nature. As stated in the introductory chapter, we cannot follow a single path from our starting point to our final goal; we must branch off not only to follow other paths but also sometimes to backtrack on them. Such is the case here, for in branching off to study the nature of light, we must backtrack into the study of wave motion because light is a wave motion. We must deal briefly with phenomena common to all wave motions in order to understand phenomena pertinent to both light and to our investigations into the structure of atoms. We will start by finding out what a wave motion is.

Wave Motion

Waves originate from centers of disturbance. For a succession of waves to be generated, a succession of disturbances must occur. This is best accomplished by a vibrating source. As a result of the disturbance, energy is transmitted from the center to a distant point with nothing of a material nature moving from the center to the distant point.

Throw a stone into the water near the shore of a quiet pond and shortly a leaf floating on the surface on the far side bobs up and down. Clearly the leaf gained kinetic energy. How was the energy transported? By the water moving from the center of the disturbance to the leaf? If so, why does not the water carry the leaf along with it? Let us try again, this time with several leaves scattered at random over the surface of the pond. We see the wave advance in all directions from the center, forming a circular wave front. As the wave reaches each leaf, the leaf bobs up and down but none shows any inclination to travel with the wave. We must conclude that the energy given to the leaves is transmitted by the surface wave, but that no water molecules are transferred from the center to any of the leaves. Only energy is transmitted from water molecules to water molecules all along the path of the wave. We might also say that only the disturbance moves outward.

Tie one end of a long rope to a fixed point, e.g., a tree, stretch it fairly taut, and give your end a shake by moving it quickly up and down several times in rapid succession. You can observe that the work you do on your end results in energy being expended at the other end. The visible evidence of this is that the tree, if it is not too big, begins to shake. Obviously, the particles in the end of the rope that you held in your hand do not travel along the rope and bump into the tree. All that travels along the rope is a series of waves (Fig. 16). The energy transmitted by the wave must be transferred from rope molecules to rope molecules the full length of the rope.

Pluck the taut string of a violin and its energy is transmitted to all of the people in a concert hall. The tympanic membranes of each of their ears are set in vibration; as a result, they hear the violin. It is not reasonable to suppose that air molecules are directly trans-

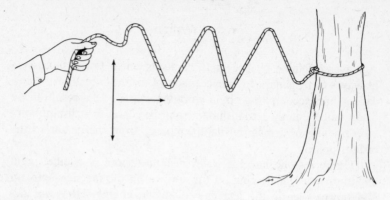

FIG. 16. *Waves in a Rope.* The vibrating source is the hand. The rope vibrates vertically as the waves travel horizontally from the hand to the tree.

ferred from the plucked string to the hundreds or thousands of ears present. We must, therefore, conclude that the energy of the plucked string is transferred from the violin to the ears by the air molecules in some way that does not include their actual movement from the center of the disturbance to the ears of the music lovers. We say that a wave—a sound wave—passed from the violin to the members of the audience, carrying energy with it.

The methods of energy transmission in the foregoing cases are clearly different from the familiar mechanical methods. The latter include transmission of energy by gears (in your automobile), belts (as in a washing machine or the fan belt of your car), chains (as on a bicycle), or a falling weight (as in a pile driver). The transference of electrical energy by means of wires, and of heat energy by means of conduction, are also mechanical in nature but less obviously so; but none of these resembles a method in which energy is transferred without anything of a material nature moving from the center of disturbance to the receiver.

The necessity of a physical medium for the water waves and rope waves is clear, for we can see the energy advance as the wave moves over the water surface or along the rope. That we need a medium for the sound waves emitted by the violin can be proved by substituting an electric bell for the musical instrument and placing it in an airtight jar from which the air is being evacuated. As the air is pumped out, the ringing of the bell becomes fainter and fainter until it cannot be heard at all. We conclude that sound waves cannot be transmitted through a vacuum. It follows that the medium transmitting the sound is air, also a physical medium. Further investigation reveals that sound waves are also transmitted by liquids and solids in the same way as they are transmitted in air.

Suppose now, while we are energy conscious, that we step outside into the bright sunlight. We wonder how the light energy and the heat energy of the sun are transmitted to us through so vast a distance. We are prepared, tentatively at least, to accept wave motion as the method, but we are at a loss for the medium. We have learned that our atmosphere extends outward at most one or two thousand miles, and that beyond we have "empty" space, space far emptier than any vacuum we can produce here on earth. If we accept the concept of wave motion, we must accept the fact that here we have a type of wave motion that needs no physical medium for its transmission, unless we wish to introduce another of those imponderables like phlogiston or caloric.[1] If we wish concrete evidence that no medium is needed, we can prepare a near-vacuum in the laboratory and pass light energy from the sun through it. We find that the transmission is actually better than it is in air. We have read in the papers about radio waves coming through empty space from distant stars. Evidently they do not need a medium for their transmission, either.

We see, then, that waves can be divided into two groups, those that require a physical medium for their transmission and those that do not. The first group includes all mechanical waves; the second includes all electromagnetic waves. We will see later that waves can be classified in other ways.

All waves, mechanical or electromagnetic, have certain characteristics in common. The most fundamental are wavelength, frequency, and velocity. We will illustrate by using a train of water waves produced by dropping stones in the same spot one after the other at regular intervals, because we can see the water waves. The high points of the waves are the *crests,* the low points the *troughs* (pronounced "troffs"). The distance between two successive crests, or two successive troughs, is the *wavelength* (Fig. 17). The number

---

[1] We will find later that such an imponderable was actually postulated for a time.

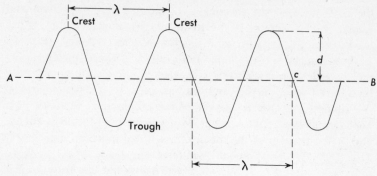

FIG. 17. *Conventional Representation of Waves.* The diagram resembles a water wave but is used for all types of waves, even light waves, which cannot be visualized under any circumstances. Since all waves originate from a vibrating source, a wave motion traveling the path *AB* may be considered to consist of a vibration from crest to trough and from trough to crest, etc., thus producing a visualizable form. The diagram is actually a graph whose curve shows the displacement at any instant along the path of the wave. λ = wavelength; d = amplitude; frequency, f, is the number of crests (or troughs) passing a given point, c, per unit time; the velocity is given by $f\lambda$.

of crests passing a given point per unit time is the *frequency*. The velocity of a wave is given by the product of the frequency and the wavelength.[2] In symbols, $v = \lambda f$ where v is the velocity, λ the wavelength,[3] and f the frequency.

The velocity of any wave depends upon the nature of the medium through which it travels—if there is a medium. For example, sound waves travel in air at about 1,100 feet per second, in water at about 5,000 feet per second, and in ice at about 10,500 feet per second. In cast iron, a dense medium of high rigidity, the speed of sound is about 15,000 feet per second, and in rubber, a

[2] If you have trouble seeing why this is so, consider a freight train passing a crossing. Suppose the number of cars passing is 20 per minute and the length of each car is 50 feet. The first car will have traveled 1,000 feet (20 × 50) by the time the twentieth car has passed. The velocity is therefore 1,000 feet per minute. The length of each car corresponds to the wavelength, and the number of cars passing per minute to the frequency.

[3] The Greek letter λ (lambda) is universally used by scientists to designate wavelength.

dense medium of low rigidity, it is only about 100 feet per second.

For electromagnetic waves the situation is quite different. Light travels through a diamond (a dense medium of high rigidity) only about half as fast as it does through air. It travels fastest through a vacuum, where its speed is about 3×10^{10} centimeters per second (*ca.* 186,000 mi/sec.). All electromagnetic waves, regardless of their frequency or wavelength, travel at this speed. Therefore, the greater the frequency, the smaller the wavelength. This follows from the equation, $v = \lambda f$. Since v is constant (either in a vacuum or in any specific medium), any increase in f must result in a decrease in λ, and vice versa.

We are all more or less familiar with the fact that water waves may be reflected from a wall, light waves from a mirror, and sound waves from a cliff or other surface. The latter we term an "echo." We are also familiar with such terms as transparency and opaqueness, terms referring to the varying degrees with which objects reflect, absorb, or transmit light waves, but we are not so likely to realize that they apply equally well to most other kinds of waves, especially to other types of electromagnetic waves. Thus, metals reflect radio waves, but glass, brick, and wood are largely transparent to them if these are not too thick. If this were not so, outdoor aerials for television and radio would always be necessary. Substances are said to be opaque if either absorption or reflection is complete or nearly so.

Waves of all kinds are also refracted; i.e., their rays are bent as they pass obliquely from one medium to another in which their speed is different. Accompanying the refraction is a change in the velocity; in fact, the velocity change is the cause of the refraction. If the boundary between the two media is at right angles to the path of the rays, there is still a change in velocity but no refraction. Thus, a stick partially submerged in water and at an angle to the vertical appears bent at the point where it enters the water (Fig. 18), whereas if it is at right angles to the water surface, it appears straight but shorter than it actually is. Thus, ponds of clear water never appear as deep as they actually are.

The pertinent point about refraction of light is that this property can be used to determine the composition of ordinary white light. If we pass ordinary white light through a glass prism (a wedge-

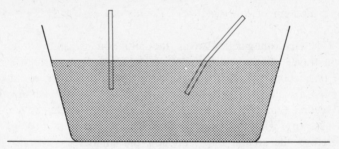

FIG. 18. *Refraction of Light*. A stick in water at an angle to the water surface appears bent because of the bending of the light rays as they change from the denser water medium to the far less dense medium of air. When the stick is vertical, no bending is observed, but the stick appears shorter than it actually is.

shaped piece of glass), the light rays are refracted on entering the glass and again on leaving it. The light leaving the glass is not white, but the colors of the rainbow (Fig. 19). Newton,[4] who was the first to perform this experiment, believed that the colors were due to the dispersion (spreading out) of the various components of white light, i.e., that white light is made up of the colors of the rainbow.

To prove this he placed another similar but oppositely oriented prism (Fig. 20) in the path of the rays coming from the first prism. These colors were recombined into white light, proving his belief. He also placed a screen with a narrow slit in it between two properly oriented prisms (Fig. 21). Through this slit he could admit any one of the colors coming through the first prism and bar the others. He allowed these colors, one by one, to pass through the second prism, oriented in different ways, to see if each could be broken up any further. He found that they could not. The colors

---

[4] Sir Isaac Newton was probably the greatest scientist of all time. He is best known for his three laws of motion (which are just as valid terrestrially now as they were the day he propagated them) and his theory and law of universal gravitation (which explained what kept the earth and the other planets in their orbits about the sun). His laws of motion include those which govern jet and rocket motions; in fact he designed a jet engine which was correct in principle, and drew diagrams illustrating the principles for putting artificial satellites in orbit. He developed some new branches of higher mathematics and wrote the first treatise on optics. Much of this work was done before he was twenty-six years old.

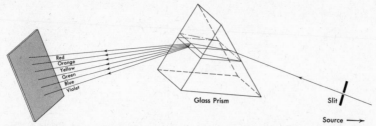

FIG. 19. Dispersion of Light by a Prism. White light, consisting of a mixture of frequencies (or wavelengths) is separated into its component colors because the rays with higher frequencies (violet) are refracted more than those with lower frequencies (red). Ordinary white light gives a continuous spectrum, for one color grades into the next with no sharp break.

emerging from the first prism are those of a rainbow—red, orange, yellow, green, blue, violet.

How do we explain these facts; i.e., how does a prism break white light up into different colors? The answer is by the refraction of the components of white light. White light consists of a band of rays with different frequencies. On entering the glass prism (a different medium) the lower frequencies (red) are refracted less than the higher. Thus, the prism sorts out the rays according to their frequencies, forming a band of colors called a *spectrum*. Actually, each spectrum color consists of a group of frequencies which the human eye translates into color. These frequencies range from 7.5×10^{14} centimeters per second (on the violet side of the spectrum) to 4×10^{14} centimeters per second (on the red side). There are also frequencies in ordinary light that are higher than the violet; these

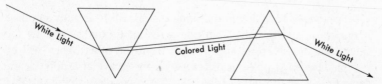

FIG. 20. Newton's Proof of Composition of White Light. White light passing through the first prism was dispersed into colored bands which were then recombined to form white light again by passing through an oppositely oriented prism.

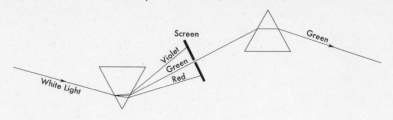

FIG. 21. *Newton's Proof that Dispersed Color Bands Are Primary.* He passed one of the colors of the continuous spectrum through another prism to see if it could be broken up into other colors. The screen with a slit was used as a selector of the desired rays.

are the ultraviolet. The human eye is not constructed to translate them to visible light, but they can be detected by other means. The frequencies immediately lower than the red are called "infrared." Our eyes do not register them as light, but our bodies detect them as heat.

This last statement should raise a question in our minds. If heat is molecular motion, why is it our bodies register the electromagnetic radiation we call "infrared" as heat rays? If our definition of heat means anything, the answer should be that these infrared rays have the ability to increase molecular motions. This justifies calling them "heat rays."

Interference

Two waves traveling in the same region will be exactly in phase if the crests and troughs from one arrive at a point at exactly the same time as the crests and troughs from the other. They will be completely out of phase if the crests of one arrive at a point at the same time as the troughs of the other. Two people walking together in step may be said to be in phase. All stages between exactly in phase and completely out of phase are possible.

That two beams of light may be combined to produce greater brightness we all know, but that two beams may be combined to produce darkness seems as unlikely as the production of silence by adding two sound waves of the same amplitude together. Yet both are possible; all that is necessary is to have the crest of one wave arrive at a point exactly out of phase with another of the same intensity (amplitude). One wave cancels the other (Fig. 22a). If the two waves arrive in phase, they reinforce each other. Their amplitudes are added together, causing increased brightness in light or greater loudness in sound (Fig. 22b). If the two waves are not completely out of phase, nor completely in phase, there will be

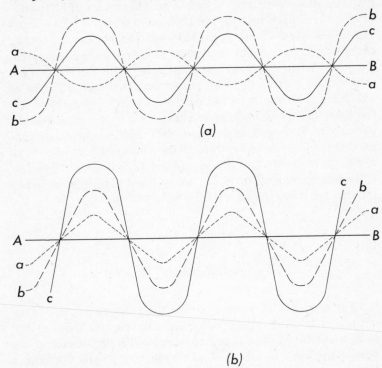

FIG. 22. *Interference of Waves Traveling the Same Path.* (a) Two waves with different amplitudes are completely out of phase. The final result is like that of a single wave, c, with an amplitude equal to the difference between amplitudes a and b. (b) Here the two waves are in phase, resulting again in a single wave, c, with amplitude equal to the sum of amplitudes a and b.

partial cancellation or partial reinforcement. The combined phenomena of cancellation and reinforcement constitute interference.

Interference accounts for the color patterns when white light, striking a thin transparent film, is reflected to the eye. The film may be a soap bubble, a film of oil on a water surface, etc. Some light is reflected from the front or top surface of the film and some light from the back or bottom surface. These two beams arrive together at the retina of an eye. The difference in the distance traveled by the two beams is equal to twice the thickness of the soap film. If this difference in path is an odd number of half wavelengths of red light, then the red component of white light will not be seen because the crests of the red wave coming from one surface of the film are canceled by the troughs of the red wave coming from the other. What is seen will be white light minus the red component—which is green to bluish-green, the complementary color of red. If the difference is an odd number of half-wavelengths of yellow light, then the yellow component of white light is canceled, etc. Because the film varies in thickness, different components are canceled out in different places, thus giving a multicolored pattern. All of the above phenomena can be satisfactorily explained by the interference of trains of waves, but not by trains of invisible particles. Interference is therefore a test for a wave motion.

Diffraction

The spreading of a wave around the edges or corners of an obstacle in its path is called "diffraction." In order for a disturbance to be transmitted from one point to another, the disturbance at one point must have an effect on all neighboring points. Consider a water wave passing through a gap in a breakwater. As the crest passes through it will obviously disturb the water on the sides of it to some extent, so that the wave spreads around the edges of the gap in the breakwater (Fig. 23).

If light from a source is passed through a tiny pinhole in a card and allowed to shine on another card placed a foot away and shielded from any other light, we will find that the spot of light on

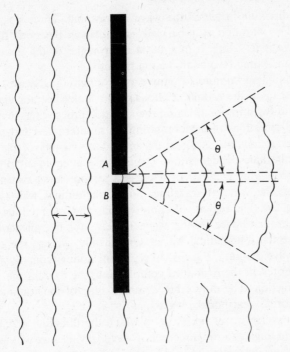

FIG. 23. *Diffraction of Water Waves.* A wall (breakwater) across a pond has a gap, *AB,* that is considerably smaller than the wavelength, λ. The waves are bent (diffracted) so much that the opening acts as a new source from which waves spread out in all directions beyond the wall.

the second card is several times as big as the pinhole. If light were *not* diffracted, the spot on the second card would be no bigger than the pinhole. This would be the case if light were composed of particles. Therefore, diffraction is a test for wave motion. The fact that light can be diffracted suggests strongly that it is a wave phenomenon. The fact that it is diffracted only slightly as it passes through the pinhole suggests that the wavelength is less than the diameter of the pinhole.

So far we have classified waves as either mechanical or electromagnetic. Waves may also be classified as longitudinal or transverse. This classification is based on the direction of vibration with respect to the direction in which the wave is traveling. Three possibilities exist. The vibration may be back and forth in the same direction the wave is traveling, it may be at right angles to the direction of travel, or it may be a combination of both.

Sound is a common example of a longitudinal wave. Superimposed upon the normal motions of air molecules are vibrations back and forth in the direction the sound is proceeding. For example, the vibrations of a violin string cause alternate condensations and rarefactions in the air in the immediate vicinity of the string. These alternate condensations (regions of increased air pressure) and rarefactions (regions of decreased air pressure) travel in the direction the wave is traveling. Such longitudinal waves "look" like Fig. 24. The regions of compressions and rarefactions propagated through space as the wave travels, not the air molecules, compose the longitudinal waves. Graphically, we use the conventional wave diagram, Fig. 17, to represent a longitudinal wave; the crests represent the regions of compression, the troughs the regions of rarefaction. The only other common type of longitudinal wave is the primary earthquake wave.

Transverse waves are those in which the direction of vibration is at right angles to the direction of wave travel. A visible example is the waves in a rope (Fig. 16). It is obvious that the molecules that compose the rope are not moving from the hand to the tree; instead, they are moving up and down, across, or transverse to the direction of wave travel. Transverse waves may be either mechan-

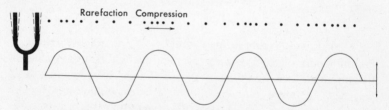

FIG. 24. *Representation of a Longitudinal Wave.* A sound wave is emitted by a tuning fork. Regions of compression of the particles composing the medium alternate with regions of rarefaction as these regions (not the particles) are propagated through the medium. Such a wave may be represented as a series of crests and troughs (as shown) in the manner of transverse waves in a rope.

ical or electromagnetic. Transverse waves can be polarized (Fig. 25), whereas longitudinal waves cannot, for the rope can vibrate in directions parallel to its own length without interference by the fence. Polarization therefore becomes a test for distinguishing between transverse and longitudinal waves. Some crystals are to light as the picket fence is to a rope, i.e., they can polarize light. Polaroid is also such a substance.

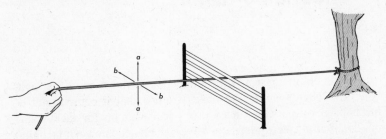

FIG. 25. *Polarization of a Light Wave.* Polarization is most easily demonstrated by a rope and a rail fence. Waves parallel to *aa* will be stopped by the closely spaced rails in the fence, whereas those parallel to *bb* will pass through without hindrance. Consider a large number of ropes vibrating in many different planes, *aa, bb,* and at various angles to *aa* or *bb.* All waves that appear in those parts of any of the ropes between the fence and the tree will have vibrations that are in the plane *bb;* none will be in the plane *aa.* This restriction to one plane of vibration at right angles to the direction of propagation is called polarization.

CHAPTER 14

Theories of Light

In our discussions of wave motion we have assumed that light is a wave phenomenon. We have assumed that it consists not of mechanical waves which need a physical medium for their transmission, but of electromagnetic waves which need no such medium. We will now briefly trace the development of the concept of light as an electromagnetic phenomenon.

The Greek philosophers and scientists could not conceive of light existing apart from the process of seeing. The realization that light is something that exists entirely independent of an eye to see it was first suggested in the eleventh century, when some evidence was produced to show that light had its origin in what was perceived rather than in the eye of the perceiver. It was not until the seventeenth century that the emission of light was viewed as a transfer of energy.

As previously stated, there are only two ways of transmitting energy. One involves the mechanical transfer of matter from the source region to another region; the other involves a wave motion, which can transmit energy without a transport of matter from the source to another region. The latter method, in the eyes of all scientists until the latter part of the nineteenth century, depended upon the presence of a medium between the source and the observer to act as the carrier of the wave motion. These two methods of transporting energy found their expression with respect to light in the corpuscular and the wave theories.

Newton believed that light consisted of particles of extremely small size which he called "corpuscles," but he believed it with no great degree of positiveness, and he failed to specify the characteristics of the corpuscles. He rejected the wave theory because he could not detect diffraction, an essential characteristic of any wave motion. Yet he knew of experiments performed by Grimaldi which indicated that light does bend very slightly as it passes an obstacle in its path, in fact, he repeated these himself. Newton attributed this bending (diffraction) to some obscure influence exerted on the corpuscles as they passed the obstacle. Even his great genius did not prevent him from misinterpreting this scientific fact. Perhaps he might not have if he had realized the smallness of the wavelength of light.

Huygens, a contemporary of Newton, was a strong advocate of the wave theory and formulated the first well-rounded version in 1678. The conflict between the two theories could not be resolved at the time, because the crucial experiment (concerning the velocity of light in different media) that might settle the matter could not be performed. According to the corpuscular theory, light should travel faster through water or through a solid than through air, while the reverse should be true of the wave theory. All waves slow down on entering a denser medium, but Newton considered his particles of light to be attracted by the denser medium and therefore accelerated upon entering it. Failure to find a way of measuring these speeds led to the general acceptance of Newton's view because of his greater reputation.

In the very early part of the nineteenth century, Thomas Young of England and Augustin Fresnel of France both demonstrated that light definitely showed both diffraction and interference effects, and the weight of opinion shifted to the wave theory. About 1850 Foucault found that the velocity of light in all media he tested was smaller than in a vacuum, thus deciding the issue conclusively in favor of the wave theory. We shall see later that this conclusion does not prove the wave theory to be unqualifiedly correct; it only ruled out corpuscles of matter which obey the laws of Newtonian mechanics and which are speeded up as they enter a denser medium.

Any satisfactory theory of light must take into account a question that had been debated since the time of the ancient Greeks, namely, does light travel at a finite or at an infinite speed? The Greeks had assumed that light had a finite speed simply because moving means going from one place to another, and this takes time. Galileo had tried without success to measure the speed of light in the simple way that speeds of finite objects were measured. That he could detect no time interval between the source and an observer several miles away could mean either that the speed was infinite or that it was too great to detect by ordinary means. The Danish astronomer Roemer settled the question of finiteness in 1676, and at the same time measured the speed with something like modern accuracy (Fig. 26). In the 1880's A. A. Michelson, an American physicist, using apparatus similar to that shown in Fig. 27 determined the velocity of light to be approximately 186,000 miles per second.

Michelson also measured the speed of light in other media and found it to be less than in air. This was in accord with the wave theory and in opposition to the corpuscular theory. He also found that red light travels at a considerably greater speed through liquids

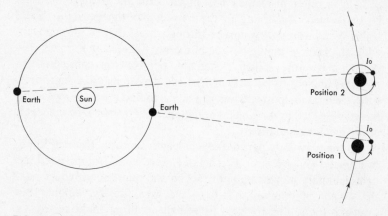

FIG. 26. *Roemer's Method of Measuring the Velocity of Light in 1676.* One of Jupiter's moons, Io, is observed to be coming out of eclipse at two different times, one when the earth is on the near side of the sun, the other when it is on the far side. Suppose the time of future appearances of Io are calculated when the earth is on the near side (position 1). When the earth is on the far side of the sun, this calculation will be found to be in error by 16 minutes (about 1000 seconds). Roemer correctly interpreted this to be the result of light having to travel across the orbit of the earth, a distance of about 186,000,000 miles, in one calculation but not the other.

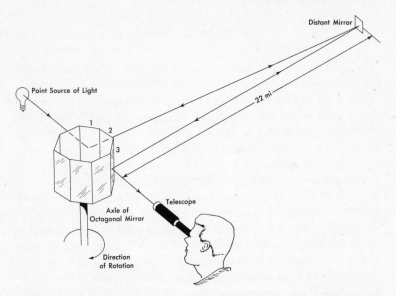

FIG. 27. *Michelson's Method of Measuring the Velocity of Light.* Light reflected from a face in position 1 travels to a distant mirror and back to the face in position 3. The octagonal mirror is spun at high speed by an air jet (not shown). If the speed is right, light from position 1 will travel to the distant mirror and back to position 3 in the time it takes a face in position 2 to travel to position 3. From these data the speed of light is easily calculated.

and solids than does blue light, yet travels at the same speed through a vacuum.[1] Michelson received a Nobel prize for his work on the speed of light.

The most modern measurement is 2.99876×10^{10} centimeters per second. The speed of light in a vacuum is a most important constant, for it enters into calculations of the sizes, distances, motions, and energies of and within atoms. It is also a basic yardstick in astronomy. For almost all purposes we may round the figures off and remember them as 3×10^{10} centimeters per second and 186,000 miles per second.

---

[1] Through air all colors travel at practically the same speed. The difference is less than 0.03 per cent.

"Luminiferous Ether"

One disconcerting question remained, that of the medium for the propagation of light waves. To the scientists of the time, waves of any kind needed a medium for their transmission. They agreed with Lord Kelvin: "If I can make a mechanical model, then I can understand; if I cannot make one, I do not understand." Without a medium a mechanical model is impossible. All other known types of waves need media for their transmission. Sound waves, for example, cannot be transmitted through a vacuum. An undiscovered medium, named the "luminiferous ether," was assumed to exist for light. It was assumed to pervade all empty space, even the space between atoms of a solid. However, its assumption was like jumping out of the frying pan into the fire, for it created more problems than it solved. Eventually Michelson performed (in 1887) what most experts in the field agreed was a crucial experiment; he found no evidence for the existence of the ether. Nevertheless, the ether concept persisted in many quarters until Einstein sent it to join the graves of phlogiston and caloric with his relativity theory in 1905.

In 1864 James Clerk Maxwell of England, one of the world's outstanding theoretical physicists, published a paper synthesizing notions about electricity, magnetism, and light, a paper that has been called the greatest scientific publication (up to that time) following Newton's *Principia*.

Maxwell's theory had its inception in Faraday's concept of electric and magnetic fields. This concept proved to be one of the greatest contributions to the understanding of electric and magnetic phenomena. The concept, greatly simplified, is as follows: The space around an electrified (or magnetized) body is changed by the mere presence of the body. The fact that this space is changed can be detected only by bringing another electrified (or magnetic)[2] body into this space. Obviously, forces are present in this space that are not present when the body is removed. This changed empty space is the electric (or magnetic) field. The existence of this field is not explainable in terms of particles or waves or fluids,

[2] A magnetic body is any body attracted by a magnet; it need not be another magnet.

imponderable or otherwise. Faraday pictured this empty space as being occupied by lines of force. To him they were a kind of string, each having a tendency to contract, and to repel neighboring lines of force.

Maxwell read the whole of Faraday's works on electricity and magnetism with admiration, and then proceeded to translate Faraday's ideas into mathematical terms. In the space surrounding a current-carrying wire, there is both an electric and a magnetic field —an electromagnetic field. If the current is *d-c and steady,* then the electromagnetic field of the wire will also be steady. Both the electric field intensity, commonly represented by the letter E, and the magnetic field intensity, commonly represented by the letter H, while constant in magnitude and direction at any one point, will be smaller and smaller as the distance to the point from the wire increases. No electromagnetic waves are propagated in space under such conditions.

Suppose, however, that we suddenly change the amount of current in the wire. This can best be accomplished by the use of alternating current, in which the electron flow [3] is continually changing both in direction and in magnitude. If we use 60-cycle alternating current, these changes take place 120 times per second. The magnitude of the current will vary from zero to a maximum value and back to zero again during the time involved in each change. (We remember that an electric current is a flow of electrons in a conductor.) What happens while the electrons in the wire are being accelerated, first positively, and then negatively? Maxwell's equations indicated that accelerated charges will send out a series of pulses of energy. Now these pulses will spread out through space like waves and with speeds equal to that of light. The source of these pulses of energy is to be found in the accelerations of the electrons. As they slow down and stop before reversing their direction, their kinetic energy is converted into the radiant energy of an electromagnetic wave. In the propagation of a mechanical wave it is the to-and-fro movement of material particles as time progresses that causes the wave to travel through the medium, whereas in an electromagnetic field it is the values of E and H that oscillate.

[3] Electrons were not known as such in Maxwell's time. He referred to them as "charged particles." Electrons, as we have already noted in Chap. 11, were not discovered until the late 1890's.

The values of E and H oscillate in directions at right angles to each other, their values reaching both zero and a maximum together. Thus, the electric wave and the magnetic wave travel through space in unison (Fig. 28). The frequency of these electromagnetic waves will be the frequency of the pulses of energy sent out by the vibrating source, whatever that source may be. For our source, 60-cycle alternating current, it will be the frequency of accelerations of the electrons in the wire, 120 per second in the case of 60-cycle current. This means that as long as electrons have nonuniform motion, whether being accelerated back and forth in the wire or being accelerated in uniform circular motion about an atomic nucleus, energy should be sent out into space by means of these wavelike radiations away from the vibrating source.

Maxwell's equations also showed that when other electrons are introduced into the fluctuating electromagnetic field, as are electrons in an antenna of a television set in the path of the waves, they absorb some of this energy as they are acted on by the electric and magnetic forces carried by the waves. These forces cause the electrons in the antenna to change their directions with the same periodicity as the transmitter's original oscillations. Thus, using mathematics alone, Maxwell predicted, without his knowing it, radio waves. Other predictions from his theory indicated that these waves should behave in all important respects like light. He was thus forced to the inferential conclusion that light is an electromag-

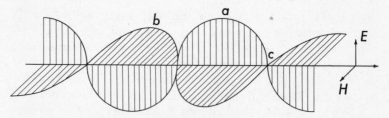

FIG. 28. "Model" of an Electromagnetic Wave. It may be viewed as an electric wave and a magnetic wave always in phase and at right angles to each other as they travel together through space. The electric wave is shown in the vertical plane, the magnetic wave in the horizontal. The electric field intensity, E, and the magnetic field intensity, H, reach a maximum (at a and b respectively) and a minimum (at c) at the same time.

netic phenomenon. He was the first to perceive that light, electricity, and magnetism are intimately related.

You should not feel defeated if you cannot picture electromagnetic waves winging their way through empty space, for scientists freely admit that they do not know what electromagnetic waves "are." The *are* is in quotes because the word implies that these waves exist as such, and we do not know that. We do know that something representing energy travels through space with a velocity of 186,000 miles per second. This energy appears to travel as a transverse wave. The evidence is that it can produce diffraction and interference effects as all waves do, and they can be polarized as only transverse waves can. One great difficulty in picturing electromagnetic waves is that no medium is needed for their propagation; thus, we have the anomaly of a wave without a "waver." The waver for water waves is the water itself, and for sound it is air. If we must have a waver for electromagnetic waves, we should assume that they are Faraday's lines of force. We know no other way to describe the phenomenon graphically.

Maxwell's theory gives us a mechanical model which can be visualized and analyzed. Mechanical models, even though they are incorrect, may give us a great deal of information that may not be obtainable otherwise. Consider a map of the world. In a sense it is a mechanical model. It is not the world, nor is it even a small replica of it. In fact, it has no real resemblance to the physical world. Yet we can learn far more about the physical world by studying this map for an hour or two than we could from years of actual exploration of the earth. Thus, we justify the use of mechanical models which may bear little resemblance to reality.

The use of Maxwell's theory advanced our knowledge of visible and invisible light far beyond what would have been possible otherwise. It has served and still does serve, as a unifying concept for many phenomena concerning light. It has been one of the most fruitful of all scientific theories, even though it cannot provide a complete explanation for all phenomena of light. Thus, Maxwellian electrodynamics was added to Newtonian mechanics to form the foundations on which all future advances in physical science would have to rest—or so it seemed at the time.

Maxwell was unable to prove that fluctuating electric currents give rise to electromagnetic waves. He neither measured the speeds of such waves nor proved that they were of the same nature as light. Why not, we may ask, set up an oscillatory current in a wire at the known frequency of red light and see if red light is emitted? The frequency of red light is 4×10^{14} cycles per second (400 million million vibrations per second). Such frequencies could not be obtained mechanically, either at that time or the present, and so direct proof was out of the question.

Maxwell pointed out that his equations did not prohibit waves of frequencies higher than those of violet light, or lower than those of red light. These waves should have all the characteristics of light except visibility. The general concept that the range of our senses placed no limit on the range of wave motions was not new, for it had long been known that vibrations of the sort that we call "sound" were not limited to those within the range of detection by the human ear. In fact, both ultraviolet and infrared radiation had been known since early in the nineteenth century. Thus, there existed the possibility that there were electromagnetic waves with frequencies low enough to be generated by apparatus available at the times. This turned out to be true, as Hertz soon showed.

In 1888, Heinrich Hertz of Germany set up a simple spark gap device (Fig. 29), which was sufficiently charged to cause a spark to jump from one electrode to the other. According to Maxwell's theory, electromagnetic waves should be sent out every time a spark jumped; and these waves should be capable of causing electrons to move the same way in a secondary circuit some distance away, provided it were "tuned" to the original circuit. The original circuit was thus a transmitter, consisting of a source, two polished metal spheres as the electrodes, and an induction coil [4] (not shown) to build up large charges on the metal spheres. The secondary circuit was a receiver, consisting merely of two similar electrodes connected to each other by a wire. Current was actually induced in this circuit, observable as a spark between the receiver electrodes, whenever the spark jumped across the transmitter electrodes.

[4] An induction coil is used with direct current, a transformer with alternating. The principle is the same, except that an induction coil must have a device to make and break the circuit rapidly. This insures that the magnitude of the current will vary. When the circuit is broken, the magnitude of the current drops to zero; when contact is made again it rises to a maximum. Thus electromagnetic waves are sent out as the electrons which constitute the current are accelerated back and forth.

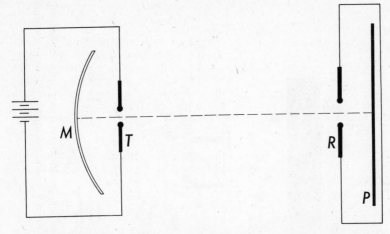

FIG. 29. *Hertz's Proof of Electromagnetic Waves.* Spark gap devices served as a crude transmitter, *T*, and receiver, *R*. A high-voltage source was necessary for the transmitter to emit a strong spark. A weak spark jumped the gap at *R* when a strong one did so at *T*. Energy was thus transmitted from *T* to *R* by means of a wave motion. *M* and *P* are mirrors used to prove the waves had the properties of light waves.

Above, we referred to the impossibility, even at the present time, of mechanically producing waves of the frequency of red light (4×10^{14} cycles per second). In the above experiment Hertz obtained about 10^8 vibrations per second. Figure 30c is a chart of the electromagnetic spectrum. We see that commercial radio broadcasts range from about 550,000 to 1,600,000 cycles per second (500 to 1,600 kilocycles). You might very well ask how such frequencies are produced. No mechanical device can be made to vibrate with anything like such frequencies.

It has been discovered that crystals, e.g., quartz crystals, have certain natural periods of vibration of their own, and these frequencies fall in the above ranges. This natural frequency is governed by the composition of the crystal, and the size and shape, in much the same way as the pitch (frequency) of a bell is determined by its composition, size, and shape. Therefore, crystals of quartz are ground to the correct size and shape to produce the desired frequency of the waves emitted from the antenna of the broadcasting

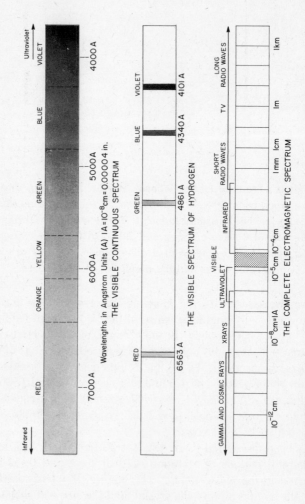

Infrared ← → Ultraviolet

RED   ORANGE   YELLOW   GREEN   BLUE   VIOLET

7000 A   6000 A   5000 A   4000 A

Wavelengths in Angstrom Units (A) 1A=10⁻⁸cm=0.00004 in.

THE VISIBLE CONTINUOUS SPECTRUM

RED   GREEN   BLUE   VIOLET

6563 A   4861 A 4340 A 4101 A

THE VISIBLE SPECTRUM OF HYDROGEN

GAMMA AND COSMIC RAYS   XRAYS   ULTRAVIOLET   VISIBLE   INFRARED   SHORT RADIO WAVES   TV   LONG RADIO WAVES

10⁻¹²cm   10⁻⁸cm=1A   10⁻⁵cm 10⁻⁴cm   1mm 1cm   1m   1km

THE COMPLETE ELECTROMAGNETIC SPECTRUM

FIG. 30. Spectra. The visible continuous spectrum (top) illustrates continuous gradation in color from deep red (left) through orange, yellow, green, blue, and violet. The bright line in the bright red, one in the light red, one in the deep yellow, and one in the blue part of the continuous spectrum.

116

station. The smaller the crystal, the higher the frequency it emits. If the size is small enough, the frequency leaves the range of the ordinary radio to that of the short-wave radio. Still smaller crystals emit frequencies in the radar range.

It might seem possible to get down into the infrared invisible light ranges by choosing still smaller crystals. The trouble is that below the radar range the crystal size is too small to handle. If we calculate—and we can—the size a crystal must be in order to emit infrared waves, we find that it must be of *molecular* size. Remembering that infrared waves are heat waves and, from kinetic theory, that heat is molecular motion, we should not be unduly surprised. Rather, we should feel gratified, for here we see how two apparently different concepts of heat, the molecular theory of heat and the wave theory of heat, can be completely reconciled by assuming that infrared (heat) waves have the ability to increase the motions of molecules.

By further reasoning and calculation we can conclude that to produce frequencies as high as those of visible light and beyond, we will need to have particles smaller than molecules and atoms, which means that no crystals can do the job. Thus, according to Maxwell's theory of electromagnetic radiation, visible light, ultraviolet light, and *any possible radiations of still higher frequencies must be emitted by oscillating electric charges within atoms.*

Further experimentation revealed that (1) conductors, such as metals, reflected the waves; (2) large, concave, metallic reflectors brought the waves to a focus just as a concave mirror focuses light waves; (3) nonconductors allowed the waves largely to pass through them, refracting them as they do so; (4) by varying the distance between a receiver and a reflector placed behind it, Hertz proved both constructive and destructive interference; (5) speed of the waves (frequency times wavelength) was about 3×10^{10} centimeters per second, the same as the speed of light in air.

Direct measurement of the velocity came in 1895. Thus, Hertz verified Maxwell's major predictions. These waves were called "Hertzian waves"; we now call them "radio waves." The fact that, unlike light waves, they will pass through opaque nonconductors if they are not too thick explains why indoor aerials for radio and television sets work very well. The fact that they are reflected or absorbed from metal surfaces explains why car radios are dimmed when crossing a metal framework bridge. In 1898, Marconi achieved reception and transmission of Hertzian waves over distances of many miles, and in 1901 sent and received them successfully across the Atlantic. Thus, radio is the result of the combined efforts of Faraday the experimenter, Maxwell the theorist, Hertz the experimenter, and Marconi the inventor and engineer. Hertz appears to have been the first to realize that the electromagnetic theory needs only a set of equations varying as to space and time, that no ether was needed for their transmission.

Further confirmation of the electromagnetic wave theory came in 1895 when Wilhelm Roentgen of Germany accidentally discovered X-rays (from *x*, the unknown in algebra). Roentgen, like so many of his fellow scientists, was investigating the nature of cathode rays at the time.

He noticed that a fluorescent screen in his completely darkened laboratory glowed whenever he operated a cathode ray tube (Fig. 7). Investigation showed that the rays had great penetrating power; i.e., all kinds of matter were transparent to them, though to different degrees. Paper, for example, was nearly perfectly transparent, and so was human flesh; even a sheet of aluminum a half-inch thick failed to stop the rays completely. A problem arose: were they streams of ultramicroscopic particles or were they trains of electromagnetic waves?

Maxwell's theory of electromagnetic radiation was at its height at the time. You will recall that, according to this theory, electromagnetic waves have their origin in positive and negative accelerations of electric charges. Now cathode rays are known to be charged particles. If they were slowed down, or stopped, as they struck the walls of the discharge tube, their kinetic energy would be transformed into some other kind of energy, most likely to electromagnetic energy. Thus, from a theoretical viewpoint, X-rays should be a form of radiation akin perhaps to the ultraviolet, and they were generally considered so almost from the time of their discovery, even though final proof did not come for seventeen years. They were then shown to have shorter wavelengths and higher frequencies than ultraviolet rays.

In the late 1890's gamma rays were recognized as emanating from radioactive elements (Chapter 11). In time they were identified as electromagnetic waves with wavelengths even shorter than

X-rays. In fact, gamma rays have the shortest wavelengths (and hence greatest frequencies) of all electromagnetic radiations. Gamma rays are also emitted in atomic bomb explosions. Both X-rays and gamma rays are harmful to human tissues—and so are the ultraviolet rays if exposure to them is excessive.

Infrared and ultraviolet radiations have been known, since early in the nineteenth century, to be parts of the solar spectrum. Shortly after Hertz had proved the existence of these electromagnetic waves that we now know as radio waves, it became apparent that visible light forms but a small part of what we now call the "electromagnetic spectrum." Radio waves had proved to have the main properties of visible light, but they were of vastly greater wavelength and lower frequency. We now commonly represent the whole electromagnetic spectrum by a line, or a bar like that shown in Fig. 30c, so that we can indicate the relationships of the wavelengths and the frequencies to one another. Wavelengths, given in centimeters are shown to the left of the scale and their corresponding frequencies on the right.

It has already been indicated that our eyes are constructed so as to receive only a limited range of frequencies in the electromagnetic spectrum. Various devices have been constructed to receive other parts of it, each being restricted to certain ranges. Radar and walkie-talkie sets, short-wave radios, television, and ordinary radio receivers, are all used to detect wavelengths greater than about 1 centimeter. Especially synthesized films of one sort or another will detect all wavelengths that are a bit shorter than a centimeter. Those wavelengths longer than that have an obvious connection with electricity, for we are all familiar to some extent with the broadcasting of radio and television waves. Those shorter than about a centimeter have no such obvious connection with electricity; we have however, already seen from Maxwell's theory that these shorter wavelengths should also be produced by electric charges that vibrate with frequencies that stagger the imagination. Vibrations of five million billion per second are necessary for green light, and of more than a billion billion per second for gamma rays. To explain how this is done by vibrators which reside within the atom is one of our ultimate aims.

CHAPTER 15

Spectra

We cannot go much further in our understanding of the fundamental nature of light, nor in our investigation of the unraveling of the structure of the atom, until we have made a study of spectra. We have already noted that white light consists of a mixture of wavelengths and that a spectrum is a band of colors produced when light is passed through a prism so that the light is dispersed into its component wavelengths.

If the light consists of a single wavelength, i.e., if the light is monochromatic, a one-color band is produced. In an analogy with sound, we may say that this one-color light corresponds to a pure tone on a musical instrument. Carrying the analogy further, we may say that white light represents a mixture of visual wavelengths, just as common noise represents a mixture of auditory wavelengths. Thus, line spectra represent certain specific wavelengths just as pure musical tones represent certain specific auditory wavelengths.

Continuous Spectra

That hot bodies should radiate heat is known to all of us. We also know that if the temperature is high enough, they also emit light. The radiator in our room may emit heat but never light; the heating element of our electric stove glows a dull red as it emits a lot of heat but little light, and the electric light bulb appears to emit more light (of the white variety) than it does heat, even though its temperature is higher than that of the heating element of the stove. We note the same phenomenon if we place a poker in a hot fire— after brief heating we detect heat radiated from it long before it is hot enough to emit light.

These are the infrared or heat waves that have frequencies too low to affect our optic nerves, but still high enough to be absorbed by our skin, where their energy is converted to molecular kinetic energy, raising the temperature of the skin. Continued heating of the poker increases the amount of heat radiated, and soon the poker begins to glow red as frequencies are emitted sufficiently high for our eyes to detect. The reason is that, as the poker gets hotter, its molecules acquire more and more kinetic energy, hence more energy is radiated from it. As heating continues, the red color gradually changes first to orange, then to yellow, and finally to white. This means that the higher frequencies responsible for the green and blue colors are increasing in amount faster than those responsible for the red. If we should continue the heating until the poker turns blue (a temperature we cannot attain in the laboratory, but which is attained in the hotter stars), the frequencies emitted that give rise to blue would be greatly increased.

From these facts we can easily make the deduction that the higher frequencies have greater energy than the lower ones. Note carefully that the total energy emitted in the infrared range does not decrease with an increase in temperature. It actually increases, as does the energy in all ranges from the red to the blue or even the ultraviolet, but red no longer determines the color that we see because of the greater abundance of the higher frequencies emitted. Thus, the intensity of light that a heated body emits increases as its temperature increases, and the color of it shifts from the red toward the blue end of the spectrum. In the interests of clarity, let us try to explain this in another way.

Without specifying its characteristics, let us call whatever it is that is emitting radiation from within the glowing body an "emitter." It is apparent that there must be enormous numbers of such emitters in the body. It should also be clearly apparent that while the temperature is low, only the low-frequency emitters emit. A higher temperature is needed to bring the high-frequency emitters into play. Thus, as the temperature rises, more emitters of all frequencies are brought into play. Since the high-frequency emitters carry more energy than the low, the radiation peak shifts toward the shorter wavelengths (higher frequencies) as the temperature rises. It is thus easy to see that the color of the light emitted by an incandescent body is an index of its temperature. The astronomer estimates the temperature of a star by observing the color of the light emitted.

If the radiation from the iron poker—or from any other solid or liquid body—is passed through a prism, a continuous spectrum is formed; i.e., there are no wavelength gaps in it even when it is extended into the ultraviolet or the infrared. There are no distinct color bands; instead, one color merges into another, as in a rainbow (see Figs. 30a, 30d). Therefore, continuous spectra are not very helpful in understanding the fundamental nature of light.

We have talked about analyzing light by passing it through a prism. A spectroscope is an instrument that allows the light to be analyzed to enter a tube through a narrow vertical slit, passes it through a system of lenses, then through the prism, then through more lenses in another tube, from which it emerges to be seen by the eye (Fig. 31). As it passes through the prism, various wavelengths are refracted (bent), the shorter ones more than the longer

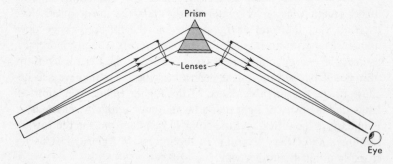

FIG. 31. *Essentials of a Spectroscope.* Light enters the prism by means of the slit at the end of the left tube. The light is dispersed by refraction into its component wavelengths (Fig. 19) by the prism, and is focused by lenses for the eye. If monochromatic light enters the slit, the eye will see a bright band or line of light whose width depends on the width of the slit, and whose position depends on the amount of refraction. The prism can be rotated so as to bring widely dispersed rays into the viewing tube.

ones (Fig. 19). The difference in the amount of bending is what causes the colors to be spread out into a spectrum, a continuous spectrum if the light is ordinary sunlight because all wavelengths are present.

Bright Line Spectra

When gases or vapors are heated to incandescence or excited to luminosity by electricity, their light gives bright line spectra when passed through a prism or a diffraction grating, rather than the continuous spectra given by all incandescent liquids and solids. The reason is that the light from incandescent gases or vapors does not contain all frequencies, but only certain ones (Fig. 30b). In other words, there are gaps in the frequencies emitted, and these gaps show up as vacant spaces between the bands of color. Consequently, what is seen when such light is viewed through the eyepiece of the spectroscope is a colored line (or several colored lines) which is an image of the slit in color. If we limit ourselves to a spectrum of the first order we can generalize by saying that we will see as many distinct slit images as there are distinct frequencies in the light being analyzed. In the case of monochromatic light, only one bright line will be seen; if there are ten different wavelengths, there will be ten different images of the slit.[1]

Bright line spectra are remarkably different with different emitters, that is, with different kinds of gases and vapors; each different kind of atom has its own characteristic pattern. Since any solid or liquid element may be converted to a vapor if it is heated to a high enough temperature, its bright line spectrum is a means of identifying it. The patterns of the spectra of the various kinds of atoms differ in the number of lines present, in the variety of the colors shown, and in the spacing of the lines, not only in the visible range but also in the infrared, ultraviolet, and X-ray regions. Thus, mercury vapor has two thin red lines, two intense lines close to-

[1] The number of colors seen when white light is analyzed will not necessarily be all of the colors of the continuous spectrum. The interfering of the complementary colors mixed in the proper portions will give white light.

gether in the yellow range, one intense line in the green, and several less intense in the blue and purple ranges. The relative order of the colors of the various lines is obviously the order in which they occur in the continuous spectrum. Sodium vapor has but two strong, closely spaced lines in the visible range, which in a spectroscope of low resolving power commonly appear as a single line. Contrast this with iron vapor which shows over six thousand lines. Clearly, the bright line spectra are the "fingerprints" of the atoms, and for that reason are often termed "atomic spectra."

The discovery that the spectrum of any one kind of atom is unique made chemical analysis by flame spectra, i.e., by heating in a hot flame, possible for many of the metals. Salts of sodium, for example, give the same yellow line as does sodium heated alone. Two new elements, cesium and rubidium, were discovered by spectroanalysis of ores containing these metals. Later, helium was discovered in the sun, some twenty years before its discovery here on earth. Astronomers are able to tell the composition of stars by their spectra. Some types of adulteration of food and other products may be detected by spectral analysis. Line spectra of gases are not produced by heating in a flame because gases cannot ordinarily be heated to incandescence. Instead, their spectra are produced by electric excitation in a gas discharge tube such as that shown in Fig. 7.

Problems of Bright Line Spectra

The great variety of patterns presented great problems to the early students of spectra, problems not resolved until after the first decade of the present century. That light is emitted by gases or vapors when their atoms are excited was known in the eighteenth century.[2] The first flame spectra were studied about 1750. Line spectra were first studied about 1800. Aside from that of Fraunhofer, not much significant work was done until the 1850's, when Kirchoff and Bunsen began the work which shortly led them to the

[2] It should be remembered that any element can be made gaseous by heating it to a high enough temperature.

conclusion that each element had its own characteristic line spectrum.

Maxwell's electromagnetic theory of light stated that accelerated charges produced the electromagnetic waves we observe as light when they strike our eyes. Charged atoms had been named "ions" by Faraday. It was recognized that either the atom or these charges had to be the emitter of the light. Something had to oscillate and give off radiation as it oscillated. But why the different wavelengths represented by the different lines, and why the exact line patterns? Why did atoms in the incandescent gaseous state emit these different bright line spectra, whereas these same atoms in the form of glowing liquids or solids emit continuous spectra only, and these all alike no matter what the element if the temperature is the same? [3] Why should sodium show only one or two (depending upon the resolving power of the spectroscope) yellow lines in the visible range, whereas iron vapor could give about six thousand lines? What complex arrangement of emitters could possibly give that many lines? Why should some closely similar elements, sodium and potassium, for example, have such different patterns? Why was there no progressive change from element to element in the periodic chart? Why should the number of lines for any one element depend upon the intensity of the heating?

Clearly, these problems could not be solved until the structure of the atom was better understood, and, conversely, it is easy to see that no picture of the atom that failed to explain line spectra could be seriously considered. Therefore, we must turn our attention to the structure of the atom in order to find the answer; but before we do so we will consider two developments concerning spectra, each of which added to our knowledge but at the same time created problems of their own.

We should also keep in mind one other fundamental problem, one more fundamental to science than the explanation of spectra or the unraveling of the structure of the atom. Energy is always associated with matter. All of the elemental kinds of matter in the whole universe are included in the periodic table. The table con-

[3] We now know that the reason they are all alike at the same temperature is that in liquids and solids, or even in the dense gaseous core of the sun, the incessant mutual collisions among the atoms blur the individual characteristics, just as springs connected together in large groups can no longer vibrate with their own frequencies.

sists of an orderly arrangement of the elements into periods and families. Why the families? Why the periods? Why the transition elements? Why do the various elements combine with each other as they do? Why do some refuse to combine except rarely? In short, what is there in the structure of atoms that governs the behavior of matter? Our search for the cause of line spectra will not be fruitful unless it also leads us to a reasonably complete understanding of the periodic table.

Balmer's Formula

In the 1870's and 1880's there was feverish research to find a numerical relation between the spacings of the spectral lines, to find some mathematical key to decode the secrets of the lines. In 1885, Johann Balmer (a Swiss schoolteacher who was neither a research scientist nor a recognized mathematician) made the first important break in the problem. By a straight trial-and-error method, he hit upon a truly remarkable formula that related the four principal (most intense) lines of hydrogen (red, green, blue, and violet) to their wavelengths (Fig. 30b). The value obtained by the use of his formula for the red line of hydrogen was within 0.02 per cent of that determined by Anders Ångström *by experiment*. This seemingly remarkable agreement by utterly different methods loses much of its strangeness when we learn that Balmer started with Ångström's experimental value and worked backward from it, juggling figures in a cut-and-try fashion until he came up with the right answer. We should note that he did not arrive at his formula by means of a theory or by mathematical analysis. Neither Balmer nor anyone else could give a reason for the success of his formula, even when applied to the other lines of the hydrogen spectrum or to lines in the ultravoilet and infrared regions of that spectrum. Balmer's formula added nothing to the understanding of the nature of light. Yet Balmer's discovery was an important milestone in the search for an explanation of bright line spectra.

Another man, Niels Bohr, explained the success of the formula. Bohr, who was born the year Balmer announced his formula, turned the spotlight back on the latter to give him deserved recognition some fifteen years after his death. This came about chiefly because of a mysterious number, 3,287,870,000,000,000. Balmer found that if he divided this number respectively by 4, 9, 16, and 25 he obtained the frequencies (not the wavelengths) of the four principal lines of hydrogen spectrum. We may not think this remarkable until we perceive that the above four numbers are the squares of 2, 3, 4, and 5. Balmer predicted that the squares of other numbers, 1, 6, 7, 8, etc., would give frequencies of lines in the ultraviolet and infrared range. Bohr showed how this mysterious number came to be calculated.

Planck's Quantum Theory

The next step toward such an understanding came through the work of Max Planck, a German physicist, about the turn of the present century. Planck was working on a problem raised by a mathematical formula obtained when one calculated the manner in which a body ought to glow when heated to incandescence. The formula was consistent with observations (experimental data) in the low frequencies, e.g., red, but was utterly inconsistent with observations in the high frequencies, e.g., violet.[4] Another formula had been developed which was consistent with the high frequencies. But why were two formulas necessary? Each could be considered half right. Planck tried to develop one that was wholly right. By trial and error he eventually found one—called his radiation formula—which agreed excellently with all of the experimental data. He now had to find some theoretical justification for this empirical formula.[5] He finally succeeded, but he was unhappy about it. Let us see why.

Planck, along with all other workers in the field, believed that spectra must be explained by the action of submicroscopic emitters

---

[4] This problem is sometimes called the "violet catastrophe."

[5] We say he "had" to do this, because no true scientist could rest content until he had. Moreover, other experts in the field would refuse to accept it until he (or someone else) had developed a theory to justify it.

(vibrators) within the atom; i.e., some part of the atom had to vibrate, and, in doing so, radiate electromagnetic waves of a particular frequency during the vibration. The radiated waves would carry the energy emitted, the amount varying with each particular kind of emitter. However, and this is the crucial point, according to Planck's theory (now called the "quantum theory") an emitter of a particular frequency f cannot send out just any part of its total energy at any instant. No matter how small the amount sent out it had to be some integral multiple of the quantity hf, where f is the particular frequency sent out and h is a constant determined experimentally.

The amount of energy in each unit radiated may be equal to hf, $2hf$, $3hf$, etc., but never a nonintegral multiple of hf, such as $1.35hf$, $2.78hf$, or the like, any more than there are 1.25 or 2.78 atoms of any element. This means that there must exist a smallest portion of radiant energy, each portion called a "quantum" of energy. It means that the rays of the sun, or rays from any other source, do not represent a continuous flow of electromagnetic waves in the visible range, but a stream of individual packets that Planck called "quanta." The process of radiation is thus assumed to be discontinuous.

The size of each packet, or quantum, is inversely proportional to the wavelength, or what is the same thing, directly proportional to the frequency. This means that there is no universal "atom" of radiant energy, since emitters of every conceivable frequency can occur in nature. A quantum of violet light thus contains more energy than a quantum of red light, because its frequency is higher. Here we have the concept of the indivisibility of packets of radiant energy somewhat analogous to the indivisibility of atoms, à la Dalton. More formally, we can state the theory as follows: *An oscillator (vibrator or emitter) possesses energy only in discrete amounts called quanta. It can gain or lose energy only in integral multiples of these quanta, i.e., in integral multiples of hf.*

It was late in 1900 when Planck presented his quantum theory as a solution to the above problems of radiation. Planck's success in formulating the new theory did not please him at all, for the price of it was a radical assumption that was not at all in accord with Maxwell's theory of electromagnetic radiation, a theory in which Planck was still a staunch believer. He did his best to destroy his own theory, for it was not very convincing either to him or to most physicists of the time.

For one thing, how could one explain interference and diffraction with the quantum theory? Furthermore, his theory, insofar as he could see, contained no solution, no picture or model, for the puzzle of line spectra. Yet the experimental facts would not allow the destruction of either theory. To be accepted the quantum theory had to have more support, support from some other source. A theory made to suit one specific set of facts can probably be adjusted to fit that particular set of facts. However, the likelihood of that theory being universally applicable is very slender unless one or more very different phenomena can be explained by the same theory. The case for the new theory is greatly strengthened if no adequate explanations of these different phenomena have yet been devised. The strengthening of the evidence for Planck's quantum theory came in 1905, from a man who was to exert a profound influence on scientific thought in the twentieth century. That man was Albert Einstein, then only twenty-six years old.

The Photoelectric Effect and the Photon Theory

About 1890 it was learned that if light of a given frequency was allowed to shine on plates made of certain metals, electric charges (later called electrons) would be ejected from the plate (Fig. 32). This ejection of electrons from metal surfaces by light of certain frequencies is called the photoelectric effect. The surfaces of conductors act as barriers to the electrons that are free to move in them.[6] To cross this barrier, i.e., to escape from the metal, electrons must acquire additional energy. If they do so by absorbing electromagnetic radiant energy, we have the photoelectric effect.

Further investigation revealed that while the ultraviolet and shorter wavelengths were effective in expelling electrons from prac-

[6] The attractions of the positive charges on the nuclei of the atoms composing the conductor prevent the electrons from escaping unless they receive energy from an outside source.

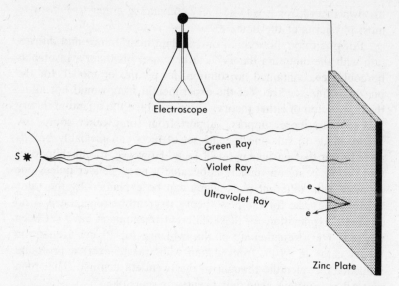

Electroscope

Green Ray

S ✹

Violet Ray

Ultraviolet Ray

e

e

Zinc Plate

FIG. 32. *Photoelectric Effect.* S is a mercury vapor lamp which emits visible light of various wavelengths along with considerable of the ultraviolet. These rays strike a zinc plate. Only the ultraviolet rays have enough energy to eject electrons from zinc. Loss of electrons leaves the plate with an excess of positive charges, as indicated by the electroscope. No matter how intense the visible light or how weak the ultraviolet, the former will not eject electrons, the latter will.

tically any metal surface, those of visible light were effective only with the alkali and the alkaline earth metals. In fact, not all wavelengths of visible light will eject electrons from sodium. No matter how intense, red light will not do so, but no matter how faint, blue light will. This can mean only that more energy is associated with the blue wavelengths than with the red, a conclusion that Planck had already reached from his work on glowing bodies.

Further experiments revealed that *for light of a given wavelength, the number of electrons ejected is directly proportional to the intensity of the light, but that the velocity of the electrons ejected is independent of the intensity.* This means that a greater intensity of light of a given frequency will result in more electrons being ejected, but will not increase the velocity of ejection. The experiments also showed that a decrease in the wavelength of light, i.e., an increase in the frequency, increased the velocity of the ejected electrons, no matter how low the intensity. In other words, a certain minimum frequency, often referred to as the "threshold frequency," is necessary to eject electrons from any one metal, and this threshold frequency is different for different metals. Ordinary light will eject electrons from cesium and rubidium, but not from zinc or iron. Furthermore, the ejection is instantaneous if the frequency is high enough, showing that no accumulation of energy is necessary.

The following analogy may help to clarify these ideas. Suppose you have a large number of bottles all the same size lined up on a fence. You stand back and throw pebbles, one at a time, and all of a certain size (analogous to frequency) and *with all your might*. If the pebbles are too small, no bottles will be knocked over. If you increase the size of the pebbles from time to time (analogous to increasing the frequency), you will eventually find a certain minimum size that will knock a bottle over and send it a certain distance. But throwing more pebbles will not send any one bottle a greater distance, but will simply knock over more bottles. Still larger pebbles (greater frequency) will send the bottles a greater distance, i.e., give them a greater kinetic energy.

The above facts could not be explained by Maxwell's theory of light. His theory required that the intensity of the radiation govern not only the number of electrons ejected but also their velocities, just as high ocean waves (corresponding to a high intensity) not only will move more pebbles on a beach than low ocean waves (corresponding to low intensity) but also will give them greater speeds. Thus, the photoelectric effect remained unexplained from about 1890 until about 1905, five years after Planck had advanced his quantum theory.

What Einstein [7] did was to apply the quantum theory to the

[7] Einstein (1879–1955) did so poorly in high school that he was asked to leave. He did graduate from another school, and entered the Federal Institute of Technology in Zurich on the basis of excellent work in mathematics. He failed to get an assistantship for graduate study, so he became a custom's clerk. However, he pursued theoretical physics as a hobby. In 1905 he published three papers, any one of which would have brought him fame. One of them was his photon theory of light. He was twenty-six years old at the time.

photoelectric problem in a simple and easy manner. Qualitatively, his method is as follows: Light is propagated through space in the form of individual packets of energy called "photons" (quanta). *On encountering an electron as it strikes a metal surface, a photon gives up its entire energy to the electron. If the amount of energy possessed by the photon is great enough, the electron will be ejected from the metal surface.* Ejected electrons are called "photoelectrons." [8] The amount of energy in each photon increases with the frequency. Greater intensity simply means more packets, more photons, not greater energy in each packet or photon. Therefore, one packet of greater frequency will accomplish what many packets of lesser frequency will not.[9]

We might wonder why Planck did not develop the photon or quantum theory of light himself, since it is based on his work. The reason is that Planck could not cut himself loose from the Maxwellian electromagnetic theory, so that he could follow the consequences of his own theory to the bitter end, no matter where that end might be. Planck was convinced that his quantum theory would set the understanding of light back a century or more, chiefly because the phenomena of interference and diffraction can be explained *only* by the electromagnetic theory.

Thus, it was left to Einstein to follow through, and Planck was by no means pleased that he did so. The photon theory as proposed by Einstein did not abandon the wave concept completely, but stated that the energy of light was not distributed over the whole

[8] If the rate of ejection of electrons is rapid enough, a feeble electric current results. This feeble current can be used to turn a switch on or off (commonly off), and thus start or stop a far stronger current flowing through another circuit. This is the principle of the "electric eye" which is so commonly used to open and close doors in supermarkets.

[9] Suppose we carry our reasoning a bit further and speculate on what might happen if the metal surface is heated strongly enough. Furthermore, let us remember that the phenomenon of electrons escaping from a metal surface for any cause whatsoever is analogous in most respects to the evaporation of a liquid. We may thus speak of the "evaporation" of electrons. As the temperature rises, the electrons gain kinetic energy, some more than others, and the additional energy needed to evaporate them becomes less. We might then assume that photons of lesser energy would eject them. This is found to be the case. In fact, as the temperature rises higher and higher, we eventually find the electrons evaporate without benefit of photons. This is called thermal emission of electrons, or thermionic emission (see Fig. 12). As in liquids, the evaporation is easier and faster with some substances than it is with others.

wave front as in Maxwell's theory, but rather is concentrated or localized in discrete small regions in the form of tiny bundles called photons. The intensity of the light is a consequence of the closeness of the spacing of the photons on the wave front. As a light wave progresses away from its source, the light becomes weaker, not because the photons lose energy, but because the distances between neighboring photons becomes greater, and the energy per unit area becomes less. Ordinarily, in experiments dealing with reflection, refraction, interference, diffraction, and polarization we are dealing with enormous numbers of photons on each wave front. They are so closely spaced that the individuality of each photon is masked, and the wave front appears to be continuous and homogeneous, just as any material solid appears to be made of continuous matter rather than of individual atoms. That is why Maxwell's theory is still most useful when dealing with ordinary problems of optics, but when we get down into the finer structure of matter, i.e., inside the atom, the finer structure of the light wave becomes important. Therefore, we will use Einstein's photon theory in our attempts to explain the relationship between light and individual atoms. You will recall that this has been our chief problem throughout this section, and that we have not yet solved it.

We must not think that the photon theory is a reversion to Newton's corpuscular theory. Newton's corpuscles were thought of as actual particles of matter, whereas photons represent bundles of energy that have no rest mass.[10] This means that once the photon stops it ceases to exist, its energy being transferred to whatever stopped it.

The photon theory has a set of problems all is own. For example, how large is the "spot" on the wave front where the photon is located? How does an electron absorb a photon? What is the meaning of frequency and wavelength if the photon is only a dot on the wave front? And so on. Our real difficulty is that we want a mechanical model that we can visualize pictorially. We can picture either waves or moving particles, but we cannot picture a wave-particle duality, something that acts like a wave under some circumstances and like a particle under others, or possibly acts

[10] It has become something of a fad to refer to photons as bullets. It is, to say the least, unusual for a bullet to cease to exist once it has stopped moving.

like both at the same time. All we can say is that the wave and the photon concepts are both needed to explain the phenomenon of light; we must learn to regard them as complementary ways of viewing one and the same process.

CHAPTER 16

The Bohr Theory of the Hydrogen Atom and Its Modifications

By 1910 it was clear that the fundamental constituents of the physical world are particulate in nature. Dalton had postulated that any mass is composed of discrete atoms or combinations of atoms that form discrete molecules. Avogadro's work had assisted him in the case of the elemental diatomic gases. By 1860 atomicity of matter was beyond dispute, and it had been established that heat is intimately associated with the motions of these atoms and molecules. The particulate nature of electricity had been suspected from the time of Faraday's work on electrolysis in the 1830's, but the final proof had to await the experiments of Thomson and Millikan. Most difficult to accept was the particulate nature of light.[1]

While light comes in individual packets of energy called photons, and is therefore particulate in nature, we must not allow ourselves to picture the photon as being a material body as an electron is. A photon may transfer its energy to an electron—as in the

[1] To avoid confusion here we need to define the word *particulate*. Webster defines it as "Existing as minute separate particles." This does not help much, for we need to know what a particle is in the scientific sense. *Scientists use it to mean the opposite of continuous.* If matter, or electricity, or light, is continuous, there can be no smallest amount that can exist. The electromagnetic wave, for example, is continuous, according to Maxwell. To speak of the "particle" nature of light without defining *particle* (as many authors do) is misleading; and to speak of the photon theory as a corpuscular theory is to use the term *corpuscle* in a sense never intended by Newton.

photoelectric effect—but when it does so, it ceases to exist. This means that it has no rest mass.[2] That energy could be transferred only in discrete packets seemed to contradict all previous ideas concerning the transfer of energy. Mechanical devices seem to convert their energy *continuously* from potential to kinetic, or from kinetic energy back to potential energy, as a swinging pendulum does. Thus, the quantum aspect of radiant energy, first advanced in 1900 by Planck in his quantum theory and extended in 1905 by Einstein in his photon theory, made little headway until Bohr used it in 1912 to formulate his theory of the hydrogen atom.

It should be realized that Rutherford's nuclear theory of the atom made no progress in explaining the old puzzle of bright line spectra, and, as has been stated before, no theory of the structure of the atom could be at all complete unless it could account for this. Rutherford's nuclear theory, therefore, applied only to the nucleus. The concept of electrons revolving about the nucleus like a minia-ture planetary system was included only because atoms possessed electrons and there was no possible way of arranging negatively charged electrons in a *stationary* pattern about a positively charged nucleus, any more than one could conceive of stationary planets ar-ranged about the sun. A theory that included normally stationary valence electrons could conceivably solve the problem of bright line spectra because energy absorbed by these electrons could cause them to vibrate and radiate the absorbed energy in accordance with Max-well's electromagnetic theory. Continuous absorption of energy from an outside source could mean continuous radiation. With normally stationary electrons impossible, the problem of bright line spectra was still unexplained, and a new problem had arisen, namely, how could an electron revolving about a nucleus, and thus being accelerated, fail to radiate electromagnetic energy if Maxwell's theory of electromagnetic radiation were to hold? [3] How-ever, the Rutherford theory was a very necessary step forward, for

[2] That the equivalent mass of a photon is sometimes given does not change matters any. Einstein's theory of relativity postulates the equivalence of mass and energy. This does not mean that a definite quantity of mass is associated with every definite quantity of energy.

[3] Any change in the motion of a body, be it a change in speed, a change in direction, or both, is an acceleration (positive or negative). A revolving body is continuously changing direction.

the structure of the nucleus certainly would be a factor in determining the nature of the arrangement of the electrons.

A solution to the puzzle was shortly presented by Niels Bohr, a young Danish physicist, just out of graduate school, who came to England to work first with J. J. Thomson and then with Rutherford in 1911. Bohr was thoroughly familiar with Planck's quantum theory and Einstein's photon theory, theories widely publicized on the Continent, but which had gained little attention in England,[4] probably for the reasons given in the previous chapter. Bohr accepted the main assumptions of Rutherford's nuclear theory and thought that he might be able to explain line spectra by combining Planck's quantum theory with it. Thus, he "married" Planck's theory to Rutherford's theory and came up, in 1913, with his theory of the hydrogen atom as the offspring. The reader is asked to keep in mind that the following discussion applies only to the hydrogen atom. Bohr chose it because it is the simplest of all atoms, containing a single charge on the nucleus and a single electron. It is easiest to test any hypothesis, theory, or postulate, by applying it to the simplest known case.

The Bohr Theory

Bohr made two startling changes in Newtonian mechanics and Maxwellian electro-dynamics by boldly stating that, 1) electrons moving around a nucleus do *not* radiate their energy and spiral into the nucleus, and, 2) electrons moving about a nucleus can do so only in certain specified orbits, orbits at specified distances from the nucleus. All other orbits were declared out of bounds. Compare this concept with artificial satellites moving about the earth. They can move in orbits of any size. To make one move in a particular orbit, all we need do is to start it off properly with the

[4] Eddington in 1936 wrote: "Let us go back to 1912. At that time quantum theory was a German invention which had scarcely penetrated to England at all. There were rumours that Jeans had gone to a conference on the Continent and had been converted; Lindemann, I believe, was an expert on it; I cannot think of anyone else."

correct speed for that size orbit. Nature will take care of the rest in accord with Newtonian mechanics. Bohr simply stated that as far as electronic orbits were concerned, Newtonian mechanics were invalid.

Both of the above changes are purely arbitrary assumptions; Bohr made no apologies for them. Adherence to the principles of Newton and Maxwell with respect to the problems of bright line spectra had long led to wrong answers, so why not abandon them? After all, Einstein had abandoned the Maxwellian theory for Planck's quantum theory in his explanation of the photoelectric effect. Moreover, the assumption is obviously in accord with the facts; electrons do not continuously radiate as they revolve. If they did, the electrons would lose all their energy and fall back into the nucleus within 1/1,000,000,000 second and the atom would cease to exist as such. But atoms do exist permanently; conventional electrodynamics must therefore be wrong, at least for atomic systems.

The specified orbits are commonly referred to as "permitted," or "stable" orbits, because in them the electron can revolve without radiating. In these orbits the electron has a certain amount of angular momentum.[5] This fixed quantity of angular momentum is given by the equation

$$mvr = n(h/2\pi),$$

where n is an integer, 1, 2, 3, etc., and h is Planck's constant. This postulates that the angular momentum of revolving electrons is quantized, i.e., it comes in particulate units whose value is equal to $h/2\pi$. Orbiting electrons may have 1 unit, 2 units, 3 units, etc., but

---

[5] Momentum may be defined as quantity of motion. The concept is necessary to explain what keeps a body moving after the force that started it is removed, e.g., a baseball after it leaves the thrower's hand, or a circular saw blade after the power has been turned off. Linear momentum applies to a body moving in a straight line; its mathematical expression is given by mv (its mass times its velocity). Angular momentum applies to a body moving in a circle; its mathematical expression is given by mvr, where r is the radius of the circle. The additional quantity r is necessary and reasonable, as we can see if we remember that two points on a revolving wheel, one nearer the center than the other (hence having different radii), have different speeds, even though each revolves through equal angles in equal time intervals.

never 1.2, 1.35, 1.4, etc., units. Suppose we transpose 2π in the above equation to the left side. We then have

$$mv \cdot 2\pi r = nh$$

We may then state the postulate in the following terms: Electrons can travel in orbits for which the linear momentum multiplied by the circumference of the orbit,[6] $2\pi r$, is equal to a whole number multiplied by Planck's constant.

One can test the adequacy of Bohr's above postulate, $mvr = n(h/2\pi)$, by applying it to the hydrogen atom in its normal, nonradiating state. Since the hydrogen atom consists of a single electron revolving about a nucleus, the radius of the electron's orbit is obviously also the radius of the nonradiating hydrogen atom. We know that its radius, calculated by entirely different methods, is about 0.5×10^{-8} centimeter. From the equation $mvr = nh/2\pi$, we see that by transposing mv to the right side, we get $r = nh/2\pi mv$. This equation can be solved by substituting quantities (numbers) obtained one way or another for the letters on the right side. There is no way of measuring the velocity of the electron in its orbit but the difficulty can be avoided by expressing v in terms of other quantities that can be determined. The radius r of the hydrogen atom turns out to be 0.53×10^{-8} centimeter, which is almost exactly equal to that calculated by very different methods. It looked as if Bohr was on the right track.

Next, Bohr postulated that *in the normal, unexcited, nonradiating atom, the electron revolves in that permitted orbit that is closest to the nucleus,* i.e., in an orbit in which n is equal to one. This orbit is sometimes referred to as the *ground state,* the state in which the energy of the electron is the smallest possible. All electrons in this state (in hydrogen atoms) have the same energy. It follows that an electron having greater energy than that in the ground state must shift to an outer permitted orbit, one with a value greater than one, and to do so it must absorb energy in the form of photons. The greater the amount of energy absorbed, the more distant the orbit occupied by the electron after the shift. Thus, electrons in outer orbits have more energy than electrons in inner

[6] The circumference of a circle is given by the diameter $(2r)$ multiplied by π.

orbits. This shift to outer orbits takes place during a period of excitation which may be accomplished in one of several ways, as follows:

If hydrogen gas is heated sufficiently to give the molecules high velocity, electrons may be knocked into outer orbits by collision with other high-velocity molecules or atoms. If the hydrogen atom is in an electric discharge tube, e.g., a cathode ray tube, a free electron which has been accelerated by high voltage may hit its electron, knocking it into an outer orbit. If the atoms of the gas are illuminated by high-energy rays (ultraviolet, X rays, gamma rays), they may absorb energy from photons. The electrons retain all or part of this absorbed energy as long as they remain in the excited state.

It also follows that to radiate a photon an electron must shift in the reverse direction, i.e., from an outer orbit to an inner one, and in doing so must radiate the same amount of energy as it absorbed in making the original outward shift (the law of conservation of energy rules here inside the atom as well as outside). The amount of energy radiated is the difference in the energies of the electrons in the two orbits. The radiated energy is in the form of a single frequency, wavelength, color. All electrons making the same shift emit light of the same color. When we see light in the hydrogen discharge tube, we are "seeing" the electrons go from higher energy states (levels) into lower energy states (levels). The color of the light seen is a composite of all the different wavelengths emitted. If the great majority of electrons are making the transition between the same two energy levels, the light we see is essentially monochromatic. When an alpha particle strikes a fluorescent screen, it boosts electrons in some of the atoms of the fluorescent paint into higher orbits. The flash of light we see is caused by the electrons returning to lower energy levels. The light seen on a television screen (which is a fluorescent screen) is caused in much the same way. Electrons ejected from the small end of the tube (by thermionic emission, footnote 9, Chapter 15) strike the screen, "knocking" electrons (in the atoms of the fluorescent paint on the inside of the tube) into higher orbits; i.e., the "screen" electrons absorb some of the energy of the thermionic electrons, and so "jump" into higher permitted Bohr orbits. Instantly they "lose" this energy as the screen electrons return to lower energy orbits.

The difference in energy between the high and the low energy orbits is emitted as photons of light. The time involved for all this to happen is of the order of a billionth of a second.

As demanded by the quantum and photon theories, the frequency of the light emitted is determined by the size of the "packet" of energy emitted. You will recall that Einstein, in explaining the photoelectric effect by means of his photon theory, stated that electrons were not ejected from metals by light shining on them, no matter how intense the light, if the frequency was too low; an electron cannot absorb just any quantity of light energy, but must absorb it in whole units (photons) whose energies are proportional to the frequency, and hence are not all the same size. If the frequency is too low, no energy at all is absorbed. Similarly, when electrons that are revolving about atomic nuclei radiate energy (by transition from outer to inner orbits), they do so in units that are proportional to the frequency, i.e.,

$$E_2 - E_1 \alpha f$$

where E_2 is the energy in the *outer* orbit (before radiation) and E_1 is that in the *inner* orbit (after radiation). If we use a proportionality constant, h, we can write

$$E_2 - E_1 = hf$$

in which f gives the frequency of the light emitted. You will recognize h as Planck's constant. The energy is radiated therefore in one fell swoop, and not continuously as the electron makes the shift from an outer to an inner orbit. If this is so, then the electron cannot spiral into an inner orbit from an outer one, but must make the change by a jump that takes place in zero time. Here again we have a departure from classical mechanics, for how can anything move through a finite distance in no time at all? Bohr says that the classical laws were not designed to explain intra-atomic behavior, and we should simply accept the idea that the electron emits a photon whose frequency is given by the above equation during a transition between two energy levels in a manner that cannot be pictured.[7] He says:

---

[7] The term "jump" is commonly used to indicate that the shift from one orbit to another is instantaneous, but it is almost certain to give us a picture of the transition, a picture that Bohr himself says cannot ever be visualized.

[This] assumption . . . appears to be necessary to account for the experimental facts. . . . [Also] we stand here almost entirely on virgin ground, and upon introducing new assumptions we need only take care not to get into contradiction with experiment. Time will have to show to what extent this can be avoided but the safest way is, of course, to make as few assumptions as possible.

In summarizing, we may say that Bohr first renounced Maxwell's electromagnetic theory, then forbade all orbits for the electron revolving about the hydrogen nucleus except certain ones, and finally he allowed electrons to "jump" from one orbit to another provided the energy differences were taken care of by the absorption or emission of single photons of appropriate frequency. The theory was really that of the relationship of the electron to the nucleus rather than a theory of the hydrogen atom. It was really a theory especially designed to explain bright line spectra of hydrogen.

How, we may ask, does it do this? Suppose we consider a gas discharge tube, such as that shown in Fig. 7, filled with hydrogen at a low pressure. When the high voltage current is turned on there will be a two-way migration of hydrogen ions toward the two electrodes. Countless collisions take place in which electrons are "knocked" (or forced to jump) into outer orbits where they have more energy than before the collision, i.e., they have absorbed specific amounts of energy during the collision. Sooner or later they will return to orbits of lower energy, emitting photons as they do so. The light emitted from all atoms in which electrons are making the same jump will be exactly the same color. Commonly, certain transitions (jumps) are more probable than others, and so a larger number of atoms are emitting the photons of a particular wavelength and frequency than any other. The Bohr theory tells us nothing about these probabilities or the resulting intensities of the light. In the case of hydrogen, the transition from the $n = 3$ orbit to the $n = 2$ orbit (Fig. 33) [8] is more probable than any other, and since the wavelengths of the photons emitted during the transition are those of red light, the hydrogen in our gas discharge tube is reddish. It is not a "pure" red, because some electrons are

[8] The values of n designate the stable, or permitted, orbits, outward from the nucleus. For no very good reason, they are called quantum numbers.

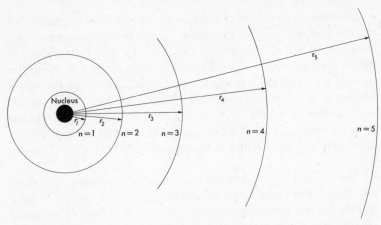

FIG. 33. *First Five Permitted (Stable) Orbits of Electron in Bohr Hydrogen Atom.* The circles represent the orbits (not drawn to scale). The radii r_1, r_2, etc., are in the ratios of 1, 4, 9, 16, and 25, that is, the radii are proportional to the squares of the value of n.

making different jumps, and so are emitting other colors, principally green, blue, violet,[9] thus adulterating the color (Fig. 30b).

The spectroscope, however, separates these colors according to their frequencies, and since the light before separation is admitted through a narrow slit, we see the bright line spectrum of hydrogen consisting of a red, a green, a blue, and a violet line, the total width being that of the slit, and the intensities being governed by the numbers of photons making the same transitions per unit time. The spectrum is a line spectrum because only a limited number of frequencies (four in the case of hydrogen) in the visible range are admitted in sufficient numbers to be visible. Dark gaps separate the lines, the widths of the gaps depending upon what frequencies are *not* emitted.

We have been assuming that the Bohr theory correctly explains how the hydrogen spectrum is produced, but we have given no

[9] In continuous spectra, all frequencies are emitted, so there are no gaps. Each color forms a band that grades into the next. Thus, red forms a band which is deepest to the left and grades into orange to the right. Red is therefore due not to a single frequency, but to a group of frequencies. If not all frequencies of the red group are present, the spectroscope will separate them into a series of red lines of somewhat differing shades.

evidence for it. True, the calculation of the radius of the first orbit and its comparison with the radius of the hydrogen atom as determined by other means was encouraging, but little more. If Bohr's third postulate, $E_2 - E_1 = hf$, is correct, then it should be possible to derive the frequencies mathematically, hence the wavelengths, of the four principal lines of hydrogen. Since these are already known, not only by measurements, but also by calculation from the empirical Balmer formula the test should be decisive, for we should now have a logical basis for Balmer's formula (Chapter 15).

We will not here follow the mathematical arguments that show how Bohr's third postulate was justified; we will be content to state that the correct wavelengths of the four principal lines of hydrogen are obtained if the proper mathematical operations are performed. The final equation is of the same general form as that of Balmer, who obtained his result by trial and error, working backward from known values for the wavelengths. Balmer had no explanation to the problems of bright line spectra.

On the other hand, Bohr first formulated the theory that explained how atoms emitted light and why the spectral lines were spaced as they were, and by the use of mathematical reasoning, he then gave a logical basis for the Balmer formula. True enough, Bohr also did some working backward from known answers obtained from experimental work, but that is commonly the way scientists work in formulating theories. Since a theory is essentially designed to explain a set of facts, and facts are obtained either through experiment or observation, this is not surprising.

It would, however, have been surprising if such an arbitrary and unorthodox theory had been widely accepted just because the frequencies of the hydrogen lines could be calculated with such a high degree of accuracy. After all, Balmer's equation allowed that to be done. What attracted profound attention was that the theory showed how that mysterious number 3,287,870,000,000,-000 involved in Balmer's work (Chapter 15) came about. If you multiply the mass of the electron (9.1×10^{-24}) by the charge on the electron raised to the fourth power ($1.6 \times 10^{-19})^4$, and that result by twice the square of π (3.1416) multiplied by the square of the conversion factor from coulombs to electrostatic units ($9 \times$

$10^{18})^2$, and then divide that final product by Planck's constant raised to the third power $(6.63 \times 10^{-27})^3$, you will get that number, and this number will agree with that obtained by experiment to within two one-hundredths of one per cent. But how, you may ask, do these quantities get into the Bohr theory? Note again the equation $E_2 - E_1 = hf$, where E_2 and E_1 are the energies of an electron in an outer and an inner orbit, respectively. These energies depend upon the mass and charge of the electron and its distance from the nucleus, and the difference between them gives the frequency of the emitted photon multiplied by h. That these quantities could be used in rational mathematical calculations to produce Balmer's mysterious number was little short of the miraculous. It guaranteed widespread consideration of his theory by specialists in the field everywhere. Its rise may truly be said to have been meteoric.

We have previously pointed out that the Bohr theory was originally designed to apply to the hydrogen atom with its lone electron. It accounted both qualitatively and quantitatively for the hydrogen spectrum. It could not account for the spectrum of the helium atom with its two electrons, nor for spectra of other atoms with larger numbers of electrons. It could, however, account fairly well for the spectrum of a singly charged helium ion, i.e., a helium nucleus with a single electron revolving about it. This means that Bohr's final equation could not be used to calculate the wavelengths of spectral lines in cases where two or more electrons revolved about a nucleus.

We might hazard a guess that the reason for this is that in the hydrogen atom the single electron moves in the constant electrical field of a nucleus carrying only one positive charge, whereas in an atom with more than one electron and more than one charge on the nucleus, each finds itself in a rapidly fluctuating electric and magnetic field caused by the motions of the other electrons. Therefore, it is not likely that the radii of their orbits could be calculated by the simple equation $E_2 - E_1 = hf$. As a result, the energies of the electrons would not be the same as they would be if they were not under the influence of other electrons and of greater charges on the nucleus. Despite these failures, the Bohr theory stands out as one of the greatest conceptions the human mind has ever devised, for it opened the way for the elucidation of the structures of these more complex atoms. It was not long before investigations began which finally resulted in the theory being modified to account for these spectra of more complex atoms.

Moseley's Concept of Atomic Number

Before summarizing these modifications—and we will do no more than that here—we will make a brief diversion to record some other investigations into the nature of the atom that were taking place at this time. We have already stated that all atoms contained electrons that revolved about a tiny nucleus which, according to Rutherford's nuclear theory, contained the great bulk of the mass of the atom. A normal atom is electrically neutral, whereas an electron carries one unit of the smallest bit of negative electricity possible. It is at once obvious that the nucleus must carry as many units of positive electricity as there are electrons revolving about the nucleus. The number of electrons in every kind of atom was not known at the time Bohr formulated his theory (1913), and no way had yet been developed for finding out. If the number of positive charges on the nucleus were known, the problem would obviously be solved. Rutherford had estimated from data gathered in his gold-foil experiment (Chapter 12) that there were in the neighborhood of one hundred in the nucleus of a gold atom. (The actual number is seventy-nine.) It was generally known that the number increased with the atomic weight. You will recall that the periodic table (Chapter 4) listed the elements in order of increasing atomic weights (except for two or three anomalies). The elements, beginning with hydrogen, had been assigned numbers in the order of their atomic weights merely for purposes of identification—just as houses on a street are assigned numbers for the same purpose. You will recall that Mendeleev left vacant spaces in his chart for elements as yet undiscovered. This numerical sequence included numbers for these vacant spaces so that renumbering would not be necessary as new elements were discovered. These numbers, as we have already stated, were originally assigned for convenience of reference; little was it realized that they also indicated both the

number of electrons circling the nucleus of the kind of atom represented by that number, and the number of electrical charges on the
nucleus.

X-rays give invisible line spectra just as visible light gives
bright line spectra. The invisible infrared and ultraviolet light also
give invisible line spectra like the X-ray spectra, spectra which are
detectable by special photographic plates. An assistant of Rutherford's, H. G-J. Moseley, had been investigating the wavelengths
of these X-rays. After he had assembled his data and analyzed
it, he found a regularity in these line spectra (Fig. 34) that

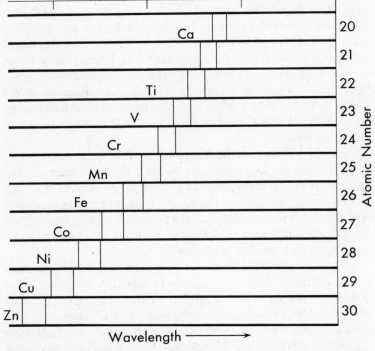

FIG. 34. *Position of X-ray Line Spectra with Respect to Wavelength.*
The spectra of all are much alike. Note that they shift toward the
shorter wavelengths as the atomic number increases. Note the regularity
of the shift. If no. 21 were unknown, the double shift would indicate a
missing element. The regularity is explained by a regular increase of
charge on the nucleus as the atomic number increases.

led him to the following conclusion: "We have here a proof that there is in the atom a fundamental quantity which increases by regular steps as we pass from one element to the next in the periodic chart. This quantity can only be the charge on the central positive nucleus." The fact that the charge on the nucleus was more fundamental than its mass (given by the atomic weight) dovetailed nicely with the Bohr model of the hydrogen atom, for the charge was basic to his theory and the mass was not.

You will recall that Mendeleev had had to make certain reversals in arranging the elements known in his time (1869) in a table according to atomic weight. The pairs that had to be reversed were argon [10] and potassium, with atomic weights of 39.9 and 39.1, respectively; cobalt and nickel, 58.94 and 58.71; and tellurium and iodine, 127.6 and 126.9. Moseley showed that the number of charges on the nucleus of the cobalt atom was 27 and that on nickel was 28, thus justifying the reversal. The other reversals were similarly justified. Certain known metals, e.g., scandium, were not available to Moseley at the time. Nevertheless, he calculated the wavelengths of its line spectra; these were later found to be almost exactly correct.

The modern concept of the atomic number of any element is, then, the number of charges on the nucleus of an atom of that element. It is also the number of protons in the nucleus, for each proton carries one positive charge. And, since the atom is neutral, it is also equal to the number of electrons surrounding the nucleus. An element could then be defined as a substance whose atoms all contain the same number of charges on the nucleus.

Just as we have found it unavoidable to refrain from speaking of the electron before we were able to relate the story of its discovery, so we are finding it equally unavoidable to refrain from using the word *proton* until we "discover" it. To "discover" it here would destroy whatever continuity and integration we have managed to keep in our story. We will accept it as a nuclear particle that carries one charge equal to that on the electron but opposite in sign. The protons in the nuclei of the lighter elements carry about half the mass of the atom. For hydrogen one proton is responsible for the whole of the mass of the nucleus, and for the heavier ele-

---

[10] Argon was not known when Mendeleev formulated his table. It was discovered in 1894.

ments the protons carry somewhat less than half the total mass. A proton and a positively charged hydrogen ion are identical.

The rest of the nucleus consists of neutral particles called neutrons. The number of protons plus the number of neutrons add up to approximately the atomic weight. We will also defer our "discovery" of the neutron to a more appropriate place in our story.

Modifications of the Bohr Theory

We can now proceed to the modifications of the Bohr theory, in the formulation of which Bohr himself played a prominent part. We have already stated that Bohr's original concern had been only with the hydrogen atom, and that the theory was highly successful with it. It failed with multielectron atoms, in large part because of the mutual repulsion of the electrons. We might further reason that, because of the greater number of charges on the nucleus, the electrons in the innermost orbit would be held more tightly than in the hydrogen atom, that the radius of this orbit would be somewhat less, and that the energies during transitions from one permitted orbit to another would be correspondingly greater. The last is a consequence of their being held more tightly by the nuclear charges.

The meteoric rise of the Bohr theory and its many spectacular successes dimmed the conflict between the two concepts of light, the wave concept of Maxwell and the particle (quantum or photon) concept of Planck, Einstein, and now of Bohr. In fact the Bohr theory did more to "advertise" the photon concept than did the work of either Planck or Einstein. The study of line spectra boomed, because the theory was designed to explain observations of them. As investigations multiplied it was inevitable that new observations would be made, and it was equally inevitable that some of these observations would require some alteration in the theory. Among them was a modification made to account for a slight motion of the nucleus, and for the relativity effect [11] of the extremely

[11] According to relativity the faster objects move the heavier they become. The effect is not detectable except at speeds of the general magnitude of the speed of light.

rapid motion of the electrons about the nucleus. Examining the spectra of glowing atoms situated in the field of a powerful magnet showed single lines splitting in two or three or even more lines. In powerful electrical fields the splitting was even greater, in some cases as high as thirty-two or even more. If we remember that *each* line results from the differences in energy permitted electrons in

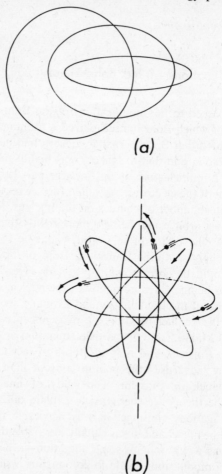

(a)

(b)

FIG. 35. (a) *Orbits Corresponding to* $n = 3$. There are three orbits, one a circle and two ellipses. (b) *Orientation of Orbits*. The four permitted orientations of the circular orbit shown in (a) above.

their allowed orbits, it is easy to see that large numbers of orbits are necessary. If these lines are very close together, we also see that the differences in energy had to be small, so small that the orbits had to differ little in radius. The original Bohr theory did not allow for such orbits. The difficulty was solved by redefining n; it no longer specified the angular momentum of the electron, but was restricted to specifying the radii of the orbits. It is called the principal quantum number. Two other quantum numbers, l and m were assigned, one to specify the shape of the orbit (Fig. 34), circular or elliptical, the other to specify the orientation of the orbit in space (Fig. 35). Later (1925) a fourth quantum number, called the spin quantum number, was added; some electrons rotated one way, and others the opposite way. The shape of the orbit, its orientation, and the direction of spin each independently affected the energy of the electron moving in it. Thus, electrons with the same value of n could have energies differing by small amounts and so give rise to spectral lines close together.

Certain problems arose from these four quantum numbers that were resolved by Wolfgang Pauli of Austria when he announced his exclusion principle in 1924: No two electrons in the same atom can have exactly the same energy. This means that no two electrons in the same atom can have the same four quantum numbers. Not more than two electrons could ever occupy the same orbit in the same atom, and these two would have opposite spins if they did so. Why this was so was unanswerable at the time. The principle was added to the Bohr theory as a special rule, a rule which was mysteriously obeyed by all electrons revolving about an atomic nucleus.

CHAPTER 17

The Wave Mechanical
Theory

Thus the original theory was patched up. However, in the early twenties holes were beginning to appear faster than the theorists could devise patches to cover them. The reasons for the holes are too complex for us to give here. Needless to say the causes were rooted in new observations. The years from 1924 to about 1928 were years in which the theory writhed in agony as one theoretician after another strove desperately to find agreement between new experimental observations and theory. In the end a new theory evolved, one that appeared to be so much different from Bohr's that its parentage can be recognized only by those who know its history.

It all began when Louis de Broglie, member of an old noble French family, gave thought to the conflict between the photon and the wave theories of light. He saw that it was folly to deny either. He had learned that in Einstein's relativity theory light, energy, and matter are linked together in Einstein's famous equation $E = mc^2$ (where E represents energy, m is the mass of a particle, and c is the velocity of light). May not light therefore have both a particle aspect and a wave aspect? May not the particle aspect be dominant under certain conditions, the wave aspect under others? [1]

[1] Perhaps in matter in relatively large chunks, the wave aspect is so overwhelmingly overshadowed by the particle aspect that the former not only cannot possibly be detected, but also is probably meaningless. As the size gets smaller perhaps the wave aspect becomes more important. It might be important in particles of atomic size if we could learn how to detect it. Perhaps in particles the size of electrons, the wave aspect is fully as important, and possibly more so, than the particle aspect.

May not waves accompany electrons just as waves accompany photons? If the latter is true, may not the *permitted* Bohr orbits be simply those orbits in which the circumference is a whole number of wavelengths? If this wave goes round and round with the orbiting electron it could continuously interfere with itself (Chapter 13). The quantum number n in the Bohr equation $mvr = nh/2\pi$ would represent the whole number of wavelengths in the orbit needed for this interference. Thus $2\pi r = n\lambda$, where $2\pi r$ is the circumference of the circular orbit and λ (lambda) is the wavelength. Starting with this a little simple algebra will give us a startling result. Let us change the c in Einstein's equation to v, the more common symbol for velocity. Thus $E = mv^2$. We will also do as de Broglie did, endow a photon with mass.[2] Now the energy of a photon is given by the equation $E = hf$, where f is its frequency and h is Planck's constant. If $E = hf$ and $E = mv^2$, then

$$hf = mv^2$$

Now the velocity of light, its frequency, and its wavelength are related in the equation, $v = f\lambda$. Dividing both sides by λ, we have

$$\frac{v}{\lambda} = f$$

Let us substitute this value of f in

$$hf = mv^2$$

This gives us

$$\frac{hv}{\lambda} = mv^2$$

Dividing both sides by v

$$\frac{h}{\lambda} = mv$$

Dividing both sides by h, we get

$$\frac{1}{\lambda} = \frac{mv}{h}$$

[2] The concept of a photon possessing such mass is not now accepted. We should not let this, however, prevent our seeing that it led de Broglie to a discovery of the first magnitude.

Writing the reciprocal of this equation, we have

$$\lambda = \frac{h}{mv}$$

Now we saw that de Broglie's equation for the permitted orbits is $2\pi r = n\lambda$. Substituting the above value of λ in $2\pi r = n\lambda$ gives us

$$2\pi r = \frac{nh}{mv}$$

Multiplying both sides by mv and dividing by 2π, $mvr = nh/2\pi$. This is Bohr's first postulate, his equation for his permitted orbits! Thus de Broglie gave a rational explanation for what Bohr obtained by a combination of mathematical reasoning and insight, high-level imagination, and a willingness to break with the Maxwell theory that here was giving consistently wrong answers. Experimental proof of the wave aspect of the electron came when Davisson and Germer of the Bell Telephone Laboratories accidentally discovered that electrons could be made to produce interference patterns. They demonstrated that electrons behaved like the waves that de Broglie predicted. Moreover, the wavelengths were of the predicted magnitude.[3]

From here on the pace becomes dizzy and the path tortuous— much too dizzy and tortuous for us to follow. The story involves such well-known men as Max Born and Werner Heisenberg of Germany, Dirac of England, Schroedinger and Pauli of Austria, and, of course, Bohr himself. These men were all theoretical physicists and mathematicians of the first order. Out of the turmoil there eventually emerged, via Schroedinger, a wave equation to replace the postulates of the Bohr theory. In it probability replaces certainty; we can never be sure where the electrons are in the atom at any particular time.[4] This is Heisenberg's uncertainty principle. This failure comes about not because of a lack of sufficiently refined techniques but because of the fact that you cannot observe electrons without disturbing them. Suppose that under certain conditions you could "see" an electron. Now you need light to "see" it,

[3] This discovery, plus the fact that these wavelengths are thousands of times *smaller* than those of visible light, or even of ultraviolet light, ultimately made the electron microscope possible.

[4] This is in contradiction to the macroscopic world of matter in which both positions and velocity are easily calculable, e.g., the velocity of the earth at a particular position in its orbit.

but when you turn on the light to do so, the electron absorbs light energy instantaneously and so moves out of its normal path. Thus, the very act of observing causes it to change both its velocity and its position. We are therefore reduced to talking about the region within the atom in which the probability of finding the electron is greatest.

In this entirely new system of mechanics, called quantum or wave mechanics and worked out in large part by Schroedinger,[5] Newton's equation $F = ma$ is replaced, insofar as electrons in atoms are concerned, by the far more complicated wave equation, with which only trained theoretical physicists may work. We will give you a peek at it, simply so you will understand why we cannot explain it here:

$$\frac{\partial^2 \psi}{\partial x^2} + \frac{\partial^2 \psi}{\partial y^2} + \frac{\partial^2 \psi}{\partial z^2} = \frac{8\pi^2 m}{h^2}(V - E)\psi$$

In this case ψ (psi) measures the strength of the wave associated with the electron, V is its potential energy, E is its total energy, m is its mass, and h is Planck's constant.

In it the uncertainty principle ruled out Bohr's definite orbits, orbits in which a definite location and velocity were assigned to each electron. In its place there was *first* substituted by Schroedinger a three-dimensional atom in which the electrons appeared as a vibrant "smear" surrounding the nucleus. These are now replaced by waves of probability, for experiments show that electrons cannot be broken (smeared) by any collision they may make. This way out was shown by Max Born. He interpreted the equation as predicting the probable average behavior of an electron in making an enormous number of revolutions. Gone were the more or less clearly defined electron jumps which explained the differences in the frequencies. How, then, were frequencies to be explained? They are needed if energy is radiated in the form of light. To clarify, Schroedinger resorted to beats in music, which are produced by the differences between two parent frequencies which alternately cancel

[5] Curiously enough. Schroedinger based his ideas not only on those of de Broglie, who was born just before 1900, but on those of a great Irish genius and theoretician, Sir William Rowan Hamilton, who died in 1865. At the age of thirteen, Hamilton had mastered thirteen languages, at twenty-eight he had transformed the science of mechanics into the form that Schroedinger found so useful.

and reinforce (Chapter 13) one another. We will not go further, for we will get into greater and greater complications if we do. Suffice it to say that, according to the new theory, energy is radiated when an electron in an atom changes its arrangement to one that has a lower energy. The equation is exactly like that of the Bohr theory, $E_2 - E_1 = hf$.

As we have previously stated, the outstanding feature of the wave mechanical theory is that it deals in probabilities, not in certainties. The probability is that the electron is more likely to be in some places than in others, that it spends more time in some places than in others. This region in which the electron is likely to be may be called a charge cloud, whose size, form, and orientation are predicted by the first three quantum numbers, n, l, and m. Pauli's exclusion principle still applies, so that any one charge cloud may be occupied by only two electrons, and these must have opposite spins. Thus the fourth quantum number, spin, is accounted for. The fundamental practical difference between this wave mechanical theory and the patched Bohr theory is that the quantum numbers, appearing naturally in the wave mechanical theory but brought in from the outside as special rules in the Bohr theory, describe charge clouds (probability distributions) rather than the definite orbits of Bohr. However, the new theory not only explains all of the things that the Bohr theory did; it also accounts for the spectra of multielectron atoms, it predicts which spectral lines will be bright and which weak, it shows that matter can be correctly described in terms of waves *and* particles, and it shows how light fits into the scheme. It accounts for all of the observable properties of even the most complex spectra—and more.

Thus the theoretical physicists have achieved what is the proper business of science, the correlation of observed facts. The facts themselves are more or less simply described. For example, the facts in a certain experiment concerning light are simple—light and dark bands are produced. These facts are brilliantly explained by the wave theory of light. The facts of the photoelectric effect are equally brilliantly explained by the photon theory of light. Now when we try to explain the bands in the above-mentioned certain experiment in terms of the photon theory, or the photoelectric effect in terms of the wave theory, i.e., when we try to correlate the observed facts of both, we are faced with a contradiction: Is light really waves or is it photons? Light is, of course, neither one nor the other, even though certain aspects of it can be described in terms of waves, other aspects in terms of particles. This is quite a different thing from saying that light is waves *or* particles or waves *and* particles. Light, we might add, is light, and light is like nothing else that we know.

All that we can ask of a theory is that it describe and explain or correlate the observed facts and predict correctly what will happen in the future. Wave mechanics deals only in probabilities. We realize that the theory does not describe or predict what a single electron will do, but does describe and predict accurately what most of the electrons in large numbers will do. This is to say that we realize that the result of an experiment on an individual atomic particle cannot normally be predicted, but that the *statistical* result of performing the individual experiment an enormous number of times, or with an enormous number of particles may be predicted with virtual certainty. Life insurance companies make profits by adhering to this principle.

There is one important by-product of the new theory, a philosophical by-product if you wish. According to classical physics you could predict the future behavior of every particle in the universe if you knew the present velocity of each, and the forces that were acting on it at the time. This implies that the future of every particle is wholly determined by its present state. Classical physics, therefore, made the universe a machine in which no room was left for free will; man, for example, could only go through his predestined motions. The wave mechanical theory, however, leaves room for free will. It leaves the universe composed of particles, many of which are electrons, and the behavior of individual electrons cannot be predicted. None has to behave as any electron has in the past. Thus the future is not in complete bondage to the past. Man has free will; fatalism had been dealt a death blow.

Unfortunately, the wave mechanical concept of the atom cannot be visualized. Yet the mind of man, being what it is, never gives up trying to visualize its concepts no matter how abstract they are. We therefore draw diagrams, some of which are shown in the following pages, to represent or to picture atoms. We must remember that none of them is actually a picture or diagram in any sense of the words. For justification the reader is referred to the analogy between a map of the world and the actual world (p. 113).

Turning again to the new three-dimensional atom, there are not only shells, but subshells (Fig. 36). In it the idea of closed shells, i.e., shells which were completely filled with electrons, was retained. The charge clouds of the electrons in each of the subshells overlapped in such a way that the final effect was that of a spherical cloud that could be imagined to resemble a shell in the true sense of the word. The number of subshells in any one shell varied from one to four, increasing from period to period in the periodic chart until the fourth. The number is not greater than four because there are not enough elements to fill more than four subshells. The electrons in any one group of subshells have energies that are nearly the same. The principal quantum number, n, designates the shell, and the orbital quantum number l designates the subshell. In the normal (unexcited) state each electron in an atom is confined to its home shell and subshell. Except under extreme conditions of excitation (such as bombardment by high-energy X rays or when subjected to heat as intense as that in the cores of the hotter stars), it is only the electrons in the outer shell that leave their home shells.

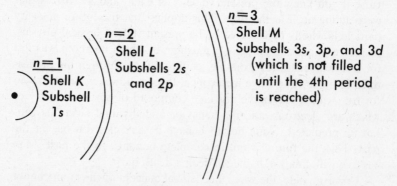

FIG. 36. *Diagrammatic Representation of Subshells in Relation to Shells.* The K shell of all atoms has only one subshell. The L shell has two, the M three, and all others have four. None has more than four because there aren't enough elements in the universe.

CHAPTER 18

Building the Periodic Table

With the use of these four quantum numbers and the exclusion principle, it was possible to "build" the periodic table of the elements. This was done before the wave mechanical theory was completed and accepted. You will remember that the four quantum numbers, n, l, m, and s, were brought in from the outside to help the theory conform more closely to experimental observations of bright line spectra. These, together with the exclusion principle of Pauli, could explain why the elements in the periodic table had to be arranged as they are. We can do no more here than indicate in a general way how this is done.

First, let us review the four quantum numbers. The principal number, n, designates the size of the orbit, i.e., the diameter of the orbit if it is circular, or the length of the long axis in the case of an ellipse. Whether it is an ellipse or a circle is given by the quantum number l (Fig. 35a). The orientation of the orbit is designated by m (Fig. 35b), and the direction of spin by s. Limitations are placed on the values of each number, as follows: (1) the values of n can only be integers (1, 2, 3, 4, etc.); (2) the values of l range from 0 to $n - 1$ (including 0); (3) the values of m range from $-l$ to $+l$ (including 0) and; (4) those of s may be $+$ or $-$ (plus or minus).

There are also a number of special rules which were put in to patch the Bohr theory. The most important is that given by Pauli's exclusion principle: No two electrons in the same atom can have the same set of four quantum numbers. Another is that there never can be more than eight electrons in the outermost shell, except for the elements in the first period in which the maximum number is two; such shells are said to be closed. A third special rule is that (in most cases) each electron must occupy the orbit with the lowest energy that is available to it.

Hydrogen and helium are the only two elements in the first period. For hydrogen $n = 1$, $l = 0$, and $m = 0$ (for the second and third limitations listed above apply here), and $s = -$ (minus). Helium has two electrons; the first has the same four quantum numbers as those of the one electron of hydrogen. The second must have at least one quantum number that is different (Pauli's exclusion principle). This is most easily accomplished by an opposite spin. We call this spin $+$ (plus). We may summarize this information as follows:

		n	l	m	s
First Period	H	1	0	0	$-$
($n = 1$ shell)	He	1	0	0	$+$

Helium closes this period because no more different sets of four quantum numbers are possible as long as $n = 1$.

Of course, the difference between hydrogen and helium is not simply the added electron with an opposite spin. Helium has a nucleus that contains two protons and two neutrons, whereas normal hydrogen has only one proton and no neutrons. These particles give helium a mass about four times that of hydrogen. As we build the periodic chart, we will add one proton and one or two neutrons to each succeeding element. We will take these additions for granted, confining our attention to the added electron only.

We pass to the second period by changing the value of n from 1 to 2. By doing so we increase the possibilities for nonduplicating sets of quantum numbers because l may now have either of two values, 0 or 1. The first element in this period is lithium; we assign the lowest of these two values of l to the added electron. Thus its four quantum numbers are $n = 2$, $l = 0$, $m = 0$, $s = -$. Since n is equal to 2, it follows from our definition of n that this added electron is in a second shell that is obviously farther from the nucleus than is the first shell. We add another electron to the next element, beryllium. It differs from the added electron of lithium only in that it has an opposite ($+$) spin. Its four quantum numbers are $n = 2$, $l = 0$, $m = 0$, $s = +$. There are no more nonduplicating sets of quantum numbers as long as $l = 0$; the first subshell of the

$n = 2$ shell is complete. For the added electron in the next element (boron), $l = 1$. The values of m may now be $+ 1$, 0, or $- 1$. For each the spin may have minus or plus values. There are therefore six elements in this subshell, boron, carbon, nitrogen, oxygen, fluorine, and neon. These two subshells complete the second period, because no more nonduplicating quantum numbers are possible as long as $n = 2$. Note that the number of electrons in this second shell increases from one in lithium to eight in neon. Eight electrons in an *outer* shell always close it, and the element closing it is always a relatively inert gas. We summarize the foregoing information in the following table:

			n	s	m	l
	First Subshell, $l = 0$	Li	2	0	0	—
		Be	2	0	0	+
Second Period, $n = 2$	Second Subshell, $l = 1$	B	2	1	−1	—
		C	2	1	−1	+
		N	2	1	0	—
		O	2	1	0	+
		F	2	1	+1	—
		Ne	2	1	+1	+

Note again that the electrons in the $n = 2$ shell are arranged in two subshells, one for each value of l. Note again that an increase of one in the value of n results in an increase of one in the *possible* values of l, and that this latter increase results in two *new* possible values of m, each with an s value of $+$ or $-$. Thus it *increases* the possible number of electrons with nonduplicating sets of quantum numbers by four in this subshell, giving us six in all. We remind you again that each element has all of the electrons, with their respective quantum numbers, of the element that immediately precedes it in the periodic table, plus one additional electron; the quantum numbers listed are those of the added electron only.

We start the third period in the same way, by assigning a value of 3 to n. There will be three possible values for l: 0, 1, and 2. This shell should therefore have three subshells but the third never gets filled in *this* period. The reason is that eight electrons get into the outer shell of argon simultaneously with the filling of the second subshell; this closes the shell with another apparently inert gas. This is illustrated in the following table:

			n	l	m	s
Third Period, $n = 3$	First Subshell, $l = 0$	Na	3	0	0	—
		Mg	3	0	0	+
	Second Subshell, $l = 1$	Al	3	1	−1	—
		Si	3	1	−1	+
		P	3	1	0	—
		S	3	1	0	+
		Cl	3	1	+1	—
		Ar	3	1	+1	+
	Third Subshell, $l = 2$	Not filled in *this* period.				

The third subshell of the third shell ($n = 3$ shell) is filled in the fourth ($n = 4$) shell, the filling of which gives rise to the first group of "transition" elements. This filling occurs *after the first subshell of the n = 4 shell* is filled, as is shown in the table following.

Note that when $l = 2$, five values of m are possible, 2, 1, 0, 1, 2, and each may have a spin value of plus or minus, giving us a total of ten different sets of quantum numbers. The capacity of this subshell is therefore ten electrons; adding these one at a time accounts for the ten transition elements, scandium through zinc. The added electrons of potassium (K) and calcium (Ca) go into the first subshell of the fourth shell, and added electrons of the six elements gallium (Ga) through krypton (Kr) go into the second subshell of the fourth period as shown in the table following.

Before the development of the revised Bohr theory we might have guessed that the reason for the similarity in physical and chemical properties of members of the same family, e.g., the alkali metals or the halogens, was due to similarities in atomic structure. The experimental evidence for these similarities in atomic structure came from the long and arduous labor of spectroscopists working on atomic spectra. The similarities, and differences in the atomic structure of four families are shown in the table below.

The members of family IA all have one electron in the outer-

			n	l	m	s
Fourth Period ($n = 4$)	First Subshell, $n = 4, l = 0$	K	4	0	0	—
		Ca	4	0	0	+
	Third Subshell, $n = 3, l = 2$	Sc	3	2	−2	—
		Ti	3	2	−2	+
		V	3	2	−1	—
		Cr	3	2	−1	+
		Mn	3	2	0	—
		Fe	3	2	0	+
		Co	3	2	+1	—
		Ni	3	2	+1	+
		Cu	3	2	+2	—
		Zn	3	2	+2	+
	Second Subshell, $n = 4, l = 1$	Ga	4	1	−1	—
		Ge	4	1	−1	+
		As	4	1	0	—
		Se	4	1	0	+
		Br	4	1	+1	—
		Kr	4	1	+1	+
	Third Subshell, $n = 4, l = 2$	Not filled in *this* period. Filled in next period.				
	Fourth Subshell, $n = 4, l = 3$	Not filled in this or the next period. Filled in the sixth period.				

most shell, those of IIA have two, those of VIIA have seven, and those of VIIIA have eight (except for helium). This is the only similarity that applies to *all* members of the same family, and at the same time is different from other main families. It is reasonable to suppose then that the essential character of the elements within a family must be determined by the number of electrons in the outermost shell. The other shells seem to make a difference in degree only, not in kind.

Note that the members of the inert-gas family,[1] except for helium,

[1] As this is written xenon tetrafluoride has been made in the laboratory, confirming a suspicion of some chemists that these "inert" gases were not as inert as generally believed. What change, if any, this fact will make in the picture here given cannot at present be predicted.

Electronic Configurations of Four Main Families

Alkali Metals Family IA	Alkali Earth Metals Family IIA	Halogens Family VIIA	Inert Gases Family VIIIA
Li 2, 1	Be 2, 2	F 2, 7	He 2
Na 2, 8, 1	Mg 2, 8, 2	Cl 2, 8, 7	Ne 2, 8
K 2, 8, 8, 1	Ca 2, 8, 8, 2	Br 2, 8, 8, 7	A 2, 8, 8
Rb 2, 8, 18, 8, 1	Ba 2, 8, 18, 8, 2	I 2, 8, 18, 8, 7	Kr 2, 8, 18, 8
Cs 2, 8, 18, 18, 8, 1	Sr 2, 8, 18, 18, 8, 2	At 2, 8, 18, 18, 8, 7	Xe 2, 8, 18, 18, 8
Fr 2, 8, 18, 32, 18, 8, 1	Ra 2, 8, 18, 32, 18, 8, 2		Rn 2, 8, 18, 32, 18, 8

have eight electrons in the outer shell. No more can be put into this shell as long as it remains the outer shell. For that reason we call it a closed shell, because eight electrons in the outer shell close the period. Two electrons in the outer shell do for helium (with only one shell) what eight do for those with more and larger shells. These eight-electron configurations, with the two-electron configuration of helium, are called stable octets; elements that have them are relatively chemically unreactive. We therefore conclude *that the essence of a chemical reaction is that the atoms involved reshuffle their electrons so that each atom has eight electrons in its outer shell, or at least has a share in the eight electrons in that shell.* Each "seeks" to attain the *stable* octet configuration. Hydrogen is an exception since it is in the first period. Two electrons form its stable "octet." The atoms of the first and second periods, the first two elements of the third period, and uranium are diagrammatically represented in Fig. 37. Subshells are not shown.

To avoid a misinterpretation we will add a word about atomic sizes. Despite the fact that the number of shells increase downward, there is comparatively little difference in the diameters of atoms. This is due largely to the fact that, as the atomic weights of the elements increase, the number of charges on the nucleus increases. The attraction of the nucleus for the electrons in the shells therefore increases, with the result that the inner shells are drawn in closer to the nucleus. Thus a cesium atom has a mass that is 132 times that of a hydrogen atom. It has six shells to hydrogen's one. It has, however, a diameter only about twice that of the hydrogen atom. It is apparent that the mass of the nucleus does not affect the diameter of an atom whereas its total charge does.

This analysis of the electronic configurations of the various kinds of atoms has several satisfying and rewarding results. We stated earlier that no theory of the structure of the atom which did not explain atomic (bright line) spectra, and at the same time the arrangement of the elements in the periodic table along with their periodicities and other regularities would be satisfactory. Moreover, these regularities should be correlated with the chemical and physical properties. That both the patched Bohr theory and the new wave mechanical theory are able to do all these things so brilliantly went far beyond the expectations of most chemists. The end result was so satisfying and so complete that P. A. M. Dirac of

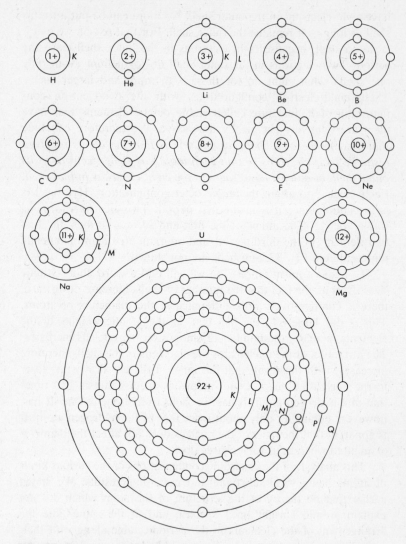

FIG. 37. *Diagrammatic Representation of Atoms of Some Elements.*
Note the numbers of shells and the numbers of electrons in each shell.
Subshells are not shown. These drawings are not to be considered in
any sense as pictures of atoms.

England, a 1933 Nobel prize winner for physics, was moved to state that "the underlying physical laws necessary for the mathematical theory of a large part of physics and the whole of chemistry are now completely known." And so it has turned out. To a very large degree the success or failure of the theories depended on their ability to explain the nature of the chemical bond,[2] to cause the fundamental mysteries of chemical reactions to disappear, to make clear the distinctions between metals and nonmetals, and to correlate other physical and chemical phenomena.

The purpose of this book is not to show how the theories do all of these things, however. We will have to be content, to say that in most, if not all *natural inorganic* chemical reactions, the final products exist in an energy state that is distinctly lower than that of the original reactants. The "inert" gases are largely inert because their completed outer shells represent the utmost in stability; no lower energy state for them is possible. Other elements, in reacting chemically either by electron transfer or by electron-sharing, tend to attain similar low-energy states. This tendency toward lower energy states is not limited to the submicroscopic world of atoms and molecules; macroscopic objects *free to do so* always seek a level where their potential energy is lowest. Thus water runs down hill, apples fall from the tree to the ground, etc.

We will take one more look at these theories before we leave them. The physical scientists had worked out these electronic configurations of atoms by means of the Bohr theory, and the four quantum numbers with certain special rules to govern their use. Why, we may ask, did they continue to work so hard to establish another theory, which was ultimately to replace the Bohr theory completely? To the scientist the reason is simple. The Bohr theory could not state why the four quantum numbers with their special rules worked. No matter how well a "gimmick" works, the true scientist is never satisfied until he knows why it works. In the patched Bohr theory the quantum numbers were brought in from the outside and "tacked" on to it. In the wave mechanical theory they arise naturally from the theory; they are a logical consequence of the wave equation. There were, of course, other failures of the Bohr theory, most having to do with energies of electrons calculated

---

[2] By the chemical bond we mean the link that holds atoms together to form molecules in compounds.

from the theory failing to agree with those obtained from experimental data. We must always remember that whenever a scientist finds that a theory or a law fails to agree with observations, he must try to find out why, because new and exciting knowledge may lie behind that failure.

CHAPTER 19

The Structure of the Nucleus

We now return to the nucleus of the atom to learn something of the energy that lies within it. Our concern with atomic structure ever since we started to discuss the Bohr theory was with the electrons and their arrangements about the nucleus. It is the distribution of energy in the outer shells that undergoes changes during chemical reactions—in fact, it is these changes that constitute a chemical reaction. During these changes the role of the nucleus was a passive one, except in the case of the hydrogen atom. Hydrogen is the exceptional atom because it is the single reactive atom with only one shell, and it is the only atom whose nucleus (in ordinary hydrogen) consists of one proton only, and has this bare proton for its positive ion. The role of this nucleus in acid-base reactions is most important.

We have seen how Moseley, by means of the progressive shift of X-ray spectra with increasing atomic number, was led to the conclusion that "there is in the atom a fundamental quantity, which increases by regular steps as we pass from one element to the next. This quantity can only be the charge on the central positive nucleus, of the existence of which we already have proof." Thus the number of charges on the nucleus is always equal to the atomic number.

These discoveries made it possible to define *an element as a substance whose atoms all have the same atomic number, i.e., the same charge on the nucleus.*

Research on the structure of the nucleus was continued by Rutherford and others, chiefly by bombarding various kinds of atoms with alpha particles (doubly charged helium ions) from a radioactive source (Chapter 12). Rutherford used them to bombard nitrogen atoms in a closed tube. The approximate atomic weights of helium and nitrogen are 4 and 14, respectively. Now a light ball with a fixed velocity that strikes a much heavier ball head-on cannot propel the latter nearly as far as it would if it struck a ball lighter than itself (law of conservation of momentum). Therefore Rutherford expected to find that the alpha particles would be stopped by collisions (even if not quite head-on) with the heavier nitrogen atoms.

To see if they would be, he placed a movable fluorescent screen in the tube. Alpha particles caused flashes of light (scintillations) to be emitted when they struck the screen. Few flashes could be observed farther than a distance of about 7 centimeters. These few, however, could be observed when the screen was as much as 30 centimeters (1 foot) away. Whatever particles caused these flashes could travel that far through the nitrogen only if they had velocities greater than those of the alpha particles, and to have such velocities meant that they had to be smaller than alpha particles. They could not, therefore, be nitrogen atoms. Neither could they be electrons. Rutherford substituted other gases for the nitrogen in the closed tube. He found that they stopped all of the alpha particles within the first 7 or 8 centimeters; no scintillations were produced if the screen was farther away. Clearly, then, the effect was one related to the particular gas, nitrogen, and, equally clearly, the particles causing the long-range scintillations were particles smaller than alpha particles. The only entities smaller than alpha particles that could produce this effect are hydrogen nuclei, which have masses about one-fourth those of alpha particles. He therefore isolated [1] some of the unknown particles and tested their behavior in a magnetic field. He found that they had the same charge and the same mass as hydrogen nuclei. They must, therefore, be hydrogen nuclei.

The next problem was their source. Rutherford first had to eliminate the possibility that they came from a source other than nitrogen nuclei. The final conclusion was that in some way the helium nuclei (alpha particles) were absorbed by nitrogen nuclei

---

[1] The separation is effected by passing the contents of the tube through electric and magnetic fields (Fig. 11).

and the product was transformed into something else. This something else turned out to be two particles, one a form of oxygen (O^{17}) and the other a hydrogen nucleus, which Rutherford named "proton." The idea that a nitrogen atom could absorb an alpha particle was bolstered by the fact that radioactive atoms eject alpha particles. Apparently the nitrogen atom had "swallowed" more than it could hold, for it immediately "spit" out, not the whole particles, but about one-fourth of it. (A hydrogen nucleus has a mass about one-fourth that of an alpha particle.)

We will attempt to clarify the preceding events. An alpha particle (helium nucleus) contains two protons which together constitute about half the mass of the particle. Each proton, therefore, is responsible for about one-fourth the mass of the particle, and each carries one positive charge. The nitrogen atom momentarily absorbs the whole particle, then ejects one proton, retaining the other three-fourths of the particle (which also contains one proton with its one positive charge). This retention adds one proton and one positive charge to the nucleus of the nitrogen atom, transforming it into an oxygen atom. (See new definition of an element, p. 169.) Thus was the old dream of the alchemist realized, the transformation of one element into another—but it was not that of a baser element into gold. It was easily proved that this newly discovered proton always carried a single positive charge, and that protons are constituents of all atomic nuclei. We can therefore again redefine an element as one whose atoms *all* have the same number of protons.

We have stated above that about half of the mass of the helium nucleus consists of two protons. What constitutes the other half? Is it a single particle with twice the mass of a proton or two particles, each with about the mass of a proton? Or even more? A case for two particles could be made from the fact that beryllium has four protons (from Moseley's work) and a mass number of 9. (The mass number of an element is the whole number nearest its atomic weight.) The remaining mass of the beryllium atom can be accounted for by five unknown particles of one unit each, but not by unknown particles of two units each. The unknown particle was first inferred to be some sort of a proton-electron combination. Such a particle would be about the right size, it would be electrically neutral, and it would account for the source of the beta particles (electrons) emitted during natural radioactivity. It also would explain why the ejection of a beta particle would increase the atomic number of the atom by one: the proton left behind, with no electron to neutralize it, would add an extra charge to the nucleus. This hypothetical proton-electron combination was named the "neutron" even before it was discovered.

The search continued for years. In 1930 Marie Curie's daughter and son-in-law (F. Joliot) were bombarding the metal beryllium with alpha particles. No protons were ejected, but a new type of radiation of greater energy than any known was detected. Again the old question was raised: was this radiation electromagnetic in character, or did it consist of a stream of particles? If particles, they had to be neutral, for the radiation was not deflected in electric and magnetic fields. The discoverers eventually concluded that it consisted of a new kind of electromagnetic waves.

In 1932 Chadwick, a former assistant of Rutherford, proved that the energy of the radiation could not be accounted for by assuming that the above new radiation was wavelike. If it were considered to consist of a stream of particles, each with a mass slightly greater than that of a proton but without a charge, all difficulties disappeared. It was soon accepted that the long awaited neutron had been discovered. A beryllium nucleus had momentarily absorbed an alpha particle, "spit out" a neutron, and had itself been transformed into a carbon atom.[2]

The long delay in detection of the neutron was due to its tiny size and its electrical neutrality. Because of these properties it has great penetrating ability; neutrons cannot be contained in any container. Since it has no charge, a neutron passing through a gas does not ionize its atoms except by a direct hit since the bulk of the atom is empty space and so does not readily lose its energy. Also it experiences no electrical force of repulsion or attraction on approaching a nucleus. In a head-on collision with a proton, all or nearly all of its energy is transmitted to the proton. The neutron has a mass number of 1 and 0 charge; it is therefore represented by $_0n^1$.

---

[2] Nuclear reactions may be summarized by an equation in which the subscripts represent the number of charges ($=$ to number of protons on the nucleus) and the superscript is the mass number. Thus, $_4Be^9 + {_2}He^4 \rightarrow {_6}C^{12} + {_0}n^1$, where $_0n^1$ is the neutron. Note that the sum of the superscripts on the left equals the sum of the superscripts on the right. The same is true of the subscripts. The above equation may be read as follows: beryllium 9 plus helium 4 gives rise to carbon 12 plus a neutron.

We can now redefine atomic mass number as the sum of the masses of the protons and the neutrons.[3] If we use the term *nucleon* to refer to either a proton or a neutron, we can say that the mass number is the number of nucleons in the nucleus. Since the atomic number, given by the subscripts in nuclear formulas, is the number of protons in the nucleus, the difference between the atomic and the mass numbers represents the number of neutrons.

The fundamental particles of the atom, electrons, protons, and neutrons, thus were all accounted for. There were, however, less fundamental particles to be discovered. Among them was the positron, a particle with the mass of an electron but the charge of the proton. The positron was discovered by observing photographs of cloud tracks (in a Wilson cloud chamber) made by "smashing" an atom with cosmic rays.[4] Along with the positron there occurred an electron. In passing through a magnetic field the paths of the two are curved in opposite directions (Fig. 38).

The explanation given, and now accepted, is that a high-energy cosmic ray, probably a gamma ray photon, entered the cloud chamber through a lead sheet, passed close to the intense electric field of a nucleus of a lead atom, and was transformed into an electron and a positron. This process is known as "pair production." The experiment described was the first known *transformation of energy into matter*. The life of a positron is very short. As it loses kinetic energy (by passing near charged particles), it will move toward an electron; they join together and annihilate each other, producing a gamma ray photon in the process. This, of course, is the reverse of pair production; it is the *transformation of matter into electromagnetic energy*.[5]

In all, about thirty other particles have been recognized. At least one fits into the theory of nuclear binding forces. Most are strange particles that have no place in the scheme of the atom as presented here. Most appear to be disintegration products of pro-

---

[3] We omit the mass of the electrons because it forms an insignificant portion of the total mass of an atom.

[4] Cosmic rays are a very penetrating radiation coming from outer space. That they are extremely penetrating means they have very high energies. Not all cosmic rays are alike. Most are probably atomic nuclei. The problem of cosmic rays is much too complex to be presented here.

[5] Positrons are not to be considered elementary particles in the same sense that electrons, protons, and neutrons are. A proton can disintegrate into a neutron and a positron.

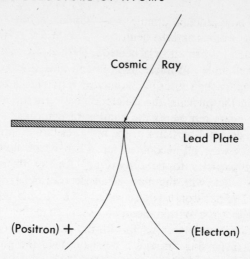

FIG. 38. *Transformation of Energy into Matter.* A cosmic ray from outer space entered the lead plate and passed close to the nucleus of a lead atom. The intense electric field of this nucleus caused the ray (probably a gamma ray photon of electromagnetic energy in this case) to disintegrate into an electron and a positron. A magnetic field below the plate causes these oppositely charged particles of matter to diverge.

tons and neutrons. The situation is rather chaotic at present. Research still goes on in the hope that order will eventually replace the present confusion.[6]

Isotopes

As far back as 1815 William Prout, an English physician, was impressed by the prevalence of whole numbers and nearly whole numbers among the atomic weights. He therefore suggested that

[6] One of the strange things about these particles is that half of them are classified as antimatter with opposite charge. They could be called antielectrons, antiprotons, antineutrons, etc. The antiparticles are produced by interactions between particles. They are short-lived, for if an antiparticle meets up with one of its counterparticles, both are annihilated by conversion of their matter into electromagnetic energy.

the hydrogen atom with an atomic weight of 1 was the fundamental particle; other atoms were made up of hydrogen atoms combined in some unknown way. The idea had to be abandoned as more accurate atomic weight determinations were made. The idea was revived in the early 1900's, however, with the discovery of isotopes.

Isotopes are different forms of the same element; their atoms have the same number of protons but a different number of neutrons. It had been known since about 1912 that not all atoms of the same element had the same atomic weight. The story goes back to the 1880's, when an investigator discovered positive rays in gas discharge tubes. These rays were ionized atoms or molecules. Experiments to determine their charge-to-mass ratio ran into trouble because not all had the same mass nor the same velocity.

The difficulty was overcome by first passing the ions through a velocity selector [7] which separates those of one particular velocity from those having other velocities. Thus we get ions whose only difference is in their masses. Once through the velocity selector, these selected ions continue to move at a uniform speed because there is no net force acting on them to change the speed. They are then passed through a magnetic field which changes their direction but not their speed. They therefore move in arcs of circles whose radii depend on the values of m, v, and e. Since v and e are the same for all, the radii depend only on m. Those with the most mass will be deflected the least and so move in circles with the largest radii (Fig. 40).

This sorting out is made apparent by allowing the deviated particles to impinge on a photographic film, where they produce lines somewhat analogous to those of spectral lines as seen in a spectroscope. The instrument that accomplishes this is called a mass spectrograph (because it separates ions according to their masses), and the series of lines is called a spectrogram. The mass spectrogram of neon, whose isotopes were the first to be separated, is shown in Fig. 39b. It reveals the three isotopes of neon with

[7] A velocity selector is an arrangement of an electric and a magnetic field at right angles to each other. The strengths of the fields are adjusted so that the net force exerted on a particular charged particle moving at a particular velocity is zero, so that the particle passes straight through without deviation. However, if particles of other velocities enter the fields, they will be deflected out of the line of flight of the particular particle (Fig. 39).

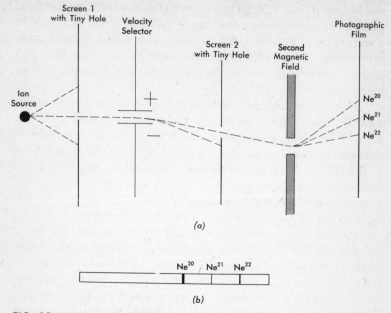

(a)

(b)

FIG. 39. (a) *Principle of the Mass Spectrograph Used in Separation of Isotopes.* Atoms must first be ionized. The screens let only those ions which strike the holes to pass through, thus insuring a narrow beam. The velocity selector consists of an electric field (shown) and a magnetic field (not shown) arranged at right angles to it. This insures that all ions passing through Screen 2 will have the same velocity and the same charge. Thus any differences in the amount of deviation on passing through the second magnetic field will be due to differences in mass only. (b) *The Three Isotopes of Neon.* The lightest is deflected the most.

their respective atomic weights. The width and intensity of the spectral lines indicate the proportions of each.

About 90 per cent of ordinary neon is Ne^{20}, which accounts for its atomic weight being close to 20 (20.2). These proportions are constant for any natural source of neon, as is also the case for all other elements.[8] For oxygen there are also three isotopes with mass numbers of 16, 17, and 18. However, 99.76 per cent of all oxygen is O^{16}. Tin has 10 isotopes. Hydrogen has three, $_1H^1$, $_1H^2$ (deu-

---

[8] An exception is lead. The reason for it being an exception will become apparent in the discussion of radioactivity.

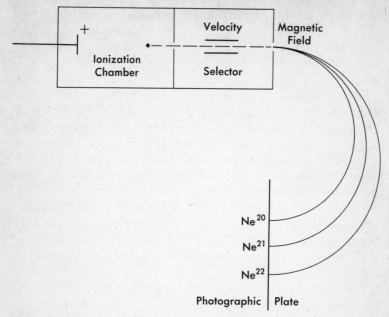

FIG. 40. *The Mass Spectrometer.* The principle is the same as that shown in Fig. 39. The curving paths are produced by a continuous deflection in a magnetic field. The lighter atoms are deflected more than the heavier ones, producing paths that are more curved.

terium), and $_1H^3$ (tritium); these latter two are the only well-known isotopes with special names. The mass of any isotope can now be calculated with very great precision (to six and seven significant figures). The mass numbers of isotopes are always within less than 1 per cent of their true masses. Chemical processes *never* separate isotopes, so that the chemist is rarely concerned with the concept.

Radioactivity

Radioactivity, as we have already indicated (Chapter 11), involves the spontaneous disintegration of certain types of atoms to form atoms of other elements by the emission of either an electron or a helium nucleus (alpha particle) from the nucleus of the disintegrating atom. In either case, the remaining part of the disintegrating atom is a new element. It is therefore a natural transmutation.

Consider the radioactive changes in the spontaneous disintegration of a uranium atom, the best known of all radioactive atoms. The emission of the helium nucleus from a uranium nucleus causes a loss of two positive charges. Hence the atomic number drops from 92 to 90. The emission also causes a loss of two neutrons so that the mass number of the new element (thorium) drops from 238 to 234. The thorium atom now emits an electron (beta ray). This electron comes from a neutron which has "decayed" into a proton and an electron. This proton raises the atomic number to 91, forming a new element, proactinium. Its mass number is the same as that of thorium, for only an electron has been removed.

Ejection of another electron from the proactinium nucleus then takes place, followed by the ejection of five helium nuclei, one after the other. In all $_{92}U^{238}$ (uranium 238) ejects eight alpha particles before the nucleus becomes stable, i.e., before radioactivity has ceased. The final product is $_{82}Pb^{206}$ (lead 206), one of several isotopes of lead. All natural elements with an atomic number higher than that of lead (82) decay into some isotope of lead. One should not conclude that all lead had U^{238} as its parent. Most that we mine has always been lead.

It was Rutherford who discovered the above sequence of events in radioactive decay. While working on the identification of alpha particles (Chapter 11), he came up with the idea that if alpha particles were ejected from atoms, other atoms of lower atomic weight would be formed. In any sample of uranium, these elements ought to be present. Analysis showed that they are. Long and careful work determined the order in which these elements of lower atomic weight were created for each isotope of uranium, U^{234}, U^{235}, U^{238}. Radioactivity is thus a natural transmutation of elements, but more nearly a transmutation of more economically valuable minerals into baser elements than the other way around.

Half-Life

Each radioactive element decays at a definite rate. A definite number of particles are emitted per second *for any given quantity of the element*. This means that if we change the quantity of the element, we change the *rate* at which the particles are emitted. Consider a number of piles of widely different masses of a radioactive element. Whether the size of the pile is 1 ounce, 1 pound, or 1 ton, *the time for half of the atoms in each pile to decay is the same*. Thus, the rate depends on the size of the pile. As the number of undecayed atoms gets less and less, the rate becomes slower and slower, so the time for complete decay to take place is infinite for each pile.

Thus, to speak of the "life" of a radioactive element is meaningless. The half-life, however, is an actual, easily determinable span of time. Nothing that man can do, either physically or chemically, to radioactive atoms can cause them to change the half-life. This half-life is a property of the atoms of a given radioactive element, and it varies enormously from element to element.

Half-Life of Radioactive Elements

U^{238}	4.5×10^9 yr	Po^{218}	3.05 min
U^{235}	7.1×10^8 yr	Pb^{214}	26.8 min
U^{234}	2.5×10^5 yr	At^{218}	1.5–2.0 sec
Th^{234}	24.1 days	Po^{214}	1.64×10^{-4} sec
Ra^{226}	1620 yr	Pb^{210}	22 yr
Rn^{222}	3.82 days	Pb^{207}	Stable
		Pb^{206}	Stable

A few moments' perusal of the above table should make it apparent that any fresh sample of a uranium-bearing mineral will consist mostly of uranium and lead. Of the other elements, only radium will be present in comparatively readily determinable quantities.

Radioactivity as a Time Clock

Consider the following facts: (1) uranium has a long half-life, 4.5×10^9 years; (2) the rate at which uranium decays is constant for any given quantity of it; (3) it is present in certain minerals formed when bodies of molten rock crystallize deep in the crust of the earth; and (4) in places these minerals may be found in fresh, unweathered igneous intrusive rocks and so contains what is left of its original uranium plus all of the lead that is the end-product of the disintegration. From these facts there arose the possibility of using the ratio of the number of atoms of lead to the number of atoms of uranium to tell the age of the sample. The earth must be at least as old as the mineral. After long and careful work to eliminate all possible sources of error, an equation was worked out that yielded reasonably satisfactory results. Thus, the *minimum* age of the earth has been determined.[8] This is approximately 3.5 billion years. The maximum age, estimated by other methods, is about five billion years.

Carbon Dating

The C^{14} (carbon 14) method is confined to more precise dating of geologic and anthropologic events of the last 50,000 years. C^{14} is a radioactive isotope formed in the atmosphere by high-energy particles from outer space (cosmic rays) which strike nitrogen atoms and transmute them to C^{14}, which has a half-life of 5,600 years. There is an equilibrium in the atmosphere between the rate of C^{14} formation and the rate of disintegration into C^{12}. All living things contain carbon obtained from the atmosphere and so also contain an amount of C^{14} in equilibrium with that in the atmosphere. When death comes to any plant or animal, the intake ceases, but the radioactive decay of C^{14} to C^{12} goes on. Thus, old, dead

[8] Other methods of minimum-age determinations exist, all by radioactivity of one sort or another. Their results are used as a check for the accuracy for the determinations listed above.

organic matter, be it straw, wood, or bones, contains less C^{14} than new wood. By measuring the concentration of C^{14}, the time since death can be computed. By this means it has been determined that the retreat of the last great ice sheet in North America began only some 10,000 years ago. In Wisconsin the advancing glacier buried living trees beneath great masses of soil and rock being transported by it. The C^{14} content of wood from these trees shows that the glacier was still advancing 10,000 years ago.

We have left a number of questions about radioactivity unanswered. We will concern ourselves here only with two. Why should one atom of a radioactive element, say uranium, emit an alpha particle at one instant, and another atom alongside of it not emit one until several billions of years later? At present we do not know. The other question is: Whence comes the energy? It was known that alpha particles are emitted at a velocity of about 10,000 miles per second, but the source of the energy which would give such velocities, was not. The study of radioactivity leads naturally to a study of the energy within the nucleus in a search for possible answers.

Nuclear Energy

The discovery that radioactive atoms emit alpha, beta, and gamma rays with enormous amounts of energy raised the exciting possibility that man could somehow tap that rich supply. Einstein had equated mass to energy in his equation $E = mc^2$ in 1905. At the time this was a mere speculation resulting from his relativity theory; there was not an experimental shred of evidence to support it. Skepticism about the validity of the equation was not so strong when it was learned that a single alpha particle was emitted with millions of electron volts (ev),[9] whereas the energy from burning carbon to form CO_2 is only about 4 ev per carbon atom. We can "shoot" electrons at helium atoms in a gas discharge tube with

[9] An electron volt is an extremely small unit of energy. We need be concerned here only with its relative magnitude. Nuclear physicists use larger units, Mev (million electron volts) and Bev (billion electron volts).

high enough energy to strip both electrons from the helium atom, converting it into an alpha particle (helium ion). This takes only about 80 ev per alpha particle. Whence come the millions of electron volts with which an alpha particle is emitted from a radioactive atom?

Consider a uranium atom with its 92 protons. Ejection of an alpha particle from it means that two protons and two neutrons are emitted as a single particle. Since all protons have the same positive charge, there is a force of repulsion between them. At the instant of ejection from the uranium atom, the two protons of the alpha particle are "feeling" the repulsive effect of the 90 protons remaining in the uranium nucleus. Is this repulsive force great enough to eject the alpha particle with a speed of 10,000 miles per second? Calculation shows that it is.

This leaves us not much better off, for we are now confronted with other questions. How can any nucleus hold together even an instant in the face of such forces? Why does one uranium atom eject an alpha particle at once and another one alongside it not do so for billions of years? Where did the uranium nucleus get its energy in the first place?

Perhaps Einstein's equation $E = mc^2$ is correct; perhaps the source of the energy is matter itself. The equation states that the energy released for *each gram* of matter that is annihilated is equal (in the proper units) to the square of the velocity of light (in centimeters per second). Thus for one gram of matter

$$E = mc^2 = 1 \times (3 \times 10^{10})^2$$
$$= 9 \times 10^{20} \text{ ergs}$$

An erg is a very small unit of energy, but 9×10^{20} ergs is an enormous amount of energy. It is enough energy to raise a 50,000-ton battleship 100 miles in the air. In a bomb it is equivalent to more than 20,000 tons of TNT. Thus the energy must be there if the equation is valid.

The first experimental check on this came in 1932 when Cockcroft (England) and Walton (Ireland) bombarded lithium atoms with high-energy protons (protons accelerated by a high voltage) in what is now called an ion accelerator. In the process alpha particles were produced. A lithium atom (atomic number 3) "swallowed" the proton, forming an unstable isotope of beryllium (atomic number 4) which instantly disintegrated into two alpha particles, as follows:

$$_3L^7 + _1H^1 \rightarrow _4Be^8 \rightarrow _2He^4 + _2He^4 + energy$$

In this reaction the alpha particles formed left the lithium at high speeds; i.e., they had a high kinetic energy. The amount of this energy could be calculated by seeing how far they could travel in air of known density. This is analogous to measuring the energy of a bullet from a gun by measuring the thickness of a board it will penetrate. The method is the same that Rutherford used in his discovery of the proton. This energy turns out to be 8.6 Mev for each, a total of 17.2 Mev for both; it may be called the output energy. Now the input energy consists solely of that of the protons used to bombard lithium atoms in a plate made of it. This turns out to be only half a Mev per proton. How could it impart an energy of 17.3 Mev to the alpha particles? Whence came the energy? Perhaps some mass was converted into energy. We can check this by calculating the masses on the two sides of the above equation.

Mass of lithium atom + mass of proton + input energy in amu (atomic mass unit) = 2 (mass of alpha particle) + output energy in amu

The input energy is the kinetic energy of the proton, and the output energy is the kinetic energy of the two alpha particles.[10]

Now *if no mass has been converted into energy,* the following equation should apply:

mass of proton + mass of Li atom = 2 × mass of an alpha particle

One of the two equations must be wrong because the output energy is greater than the input energy. Let us substitute the actual masses in each, doing so in the latter equation first.

$$1.0076 \ amu + 7.0166 \ amu = 4.0028 \ amu + 4.0028 \ amu$$
$$8.0242 \ amu = 8.0056 \ amu + ?$$

The difference is

$$8.0242 - 8.0056 = 0.0186 \ amu$$

[10] One atom of C^{12} (carbon 12) weighs $12/6 \times 10^{23}$ gram. One-twelfth of this weight is one atomic mass unit. It is equal to 1.66×10^{-24} gram. If 1 amu of matter is converted into energy, 931 Mev are released.

Note the question mark. Does it have any significance? It wouldn't, if we could explain the difference, 0.0186 amu, by experimental error. The masses of atomic nuclei are now known to five and six decimal places (by means of the mass spectrograph, Fig. 40), although we have listed them only to four. The difference here is in the second. Thus it cannot be accounted for by experimental error. Perhaps some mass was converted to energy. Let us substitute in the first equation above to see if this is so.

$$1.00760 \text{ amu} + 7.01657 \text{ amu} + 0.00016 \text{ amu}$$
$$\text{(mass of proton)} \qquad \text{(mass of Li atom)} \qquad \text{(input energy)}$$

$$= 2(4.00278) \text{ amu} + 0.01847 \text{ amu} [11]$$
$$\text{(mass of two alpha particles)} \qquad \text{(output energy)}$$

The total amu on both sides is

$$8.02433 \text{ amu} = 8.02403 \text{ amu}.$$

The difference here, in the fourth decimal place, is within the limits of experimental error.

Let us now take the difference in masses, 0.0186 amu, on the two sides of the last equation in our *first* calculation and convert it to energy by means of Einstein's mass-energy equation to see if there is agreement with the observed energies of the alpha particles: Using the conversion factor of 931 Mev = 1 amu (footnote 10)

$$0.0186 \times 931 = 17.3 \text{ Mev}$$

This turns out to be in very close agreement with the measured energies of the two alpha particles, 17.2 Mev, as determined by the Cockcroft-Walton experiment. Einstein's mass-energy equation seemed valid. To check, Cockcroft and Walton bombarded fluorine with protons. Again they measured the energies of the particles involved and set up the mass-energy equation to find the energy liberated. They then divided the energy between the particles in accordance with the laws of conservation of momentum and energy. The agreement between that measured and the computed values were as good as in the previous case. Einstein's mass-energy equation was no longer subject to doubt. Thus, the great significance of

[11] The input energy is about 0.5 Mev, equivalent to 0.00054 amu. The output energy is about 17.2 Mev, equivalent to 0.01847 amu.

the Cockcroft-Walton experiment, the first known conversion of mass into energy, was established.

Stability of Nuclei

We still wonder, however, how the protons and the neutrons can remain tightly packed together to form stable nuclei. Let us compare the combined masses of two free protons and two free neutrons with the mass of a helium nucleus, which consists of four such particles bound together in some way:

Mass of two free protons:

$$2 \times 1.00814 = 2.01628 \text{ amu}$$

Mass of two free neutrons:

$$2 \times 1.00898 = 2.01796 \text{ amu}$$

Total Mass $\qquad = 4.03424 \text{ amu}$

The mass of the helium nucleus, composed of two protons and two neutrons, is 4.00387 amu. The difference is 0.03037 amu. This means that when two protons and two neutrons combine to form a helium nucleus, there is a loss of 0.03037 amu. Now a helium nucleus (alpha particle) is very stable. We have seen that they can be used to smash other atoms without themselves being broken up. This must mean that a great deal of energy is used to hold them together. This 0.03037 amu corresponds to $0.03037 \times 931 = 28.3$ Mev. This is the energy that holds the four particles together in the helium nucleus. It is called the binding energy.[12]

[12] Let us calculate this energy in other units. How much energy is released if 2.01628 gm of protons and 2.01796 gm of neutrons were to combine to form 4.00307 gm of alpha particles? The difference in mass is 0.03037 gm.

$$E = mc^2 = 0.03037 \times (3 \times 10^{10})^2 = 2.73 \times 10^{19} \text{ ergs}$$
$$= 2.73 \times 10^{12} \text{ joules}$$
$$= \frac{2.73 \times 10^{12} \text{ joules}}{4.18 \text{ joules/cal}} = 653 \text{ billion cal}$$
$$= 26 \text{ million kw-hr}$$

Much as this may convince us that the energy to hold stable nuclei together can be accounted for, it still fails to offer any satisfying pictorial model as to how it overcomes the mutual repulsion of the protons or how neutrons can be attracted either to protons or to one another. Gravitational attractions are billions of billions times too small.

To understand the problem better, let us consider the nucleus of deuterium, an isotope of hydrogen ($_1H^2$). It contains one proton and one neutron, and so is the simplest nucleus that contains a neutron. Deuterium is a very stable isotope; like the helium nucleus, its mass is less than the combined mass of a free proton and a free neutron. There is no force of electrical attraction between the proton and the neutron in deuterium. Yet there *must* be a force of attraction of some kind between them. Whether we understand the nature of this attraction or not, we must accept the concept of very large attractive forces between protons and neutrons when they are extremely close together.

We have used the relationship between the combined masses of free protons and free neutrons and the mass of a nucleus to explain the stability of nuclei. We note that stability is increased by a decrease in mass, just as atoms with their electrons in a lower energy state are more stable than when they are in a higher energy state. Now let us see if we can also use the mass difference to explain instability. Let us begin with the neutron.

A free neutron has a mass equal to 1.008986 amu. A free proton has 1.007595 amu, and an electron, 0.000550 amu. Together the mass of the proton and the electron is 1.008145 amu. This is 0.000841 amu *less* than the mass of the neutron; i.e., a neutron has a *greater* mass than the sum of its free parts. The neutron may therefore be considered as existing in a *higher energy* state than the proton and the electron. We should suspect, then, that the neutron should be less stable than either a proton or an electron. This turns out to be the case, for the half-life of a neutron is about thirteen

---

Since this is the energy released when about 2 gm of neutrons and about 2 gm of protons are combined to form 4 gm of helium nuclei, it is the energy that must be supplied to break up 6×10^{23} nuclei of helium atoms (since 4 gm of helium is one mole and there are 6×10^{23} particles in a mole of any element) into free protons and free neutrons. In the process this *energy* would be converted into matter. It is no wonder that alpha particles are so stable.

minutes, whereas protons and electrons can exist in the free state forever. We remember that a radioactive atom may eject a beta ray (electron) with a very high energy, and that a proton was created in the process without changing the mass number of the atom. The energy represented by the 0.000841 amu difference mentioned above corresponds to the energy of the emitted beta ray. Here we have another confirmation of the concept that the beta ray is ejected *from a neutron* in radioactive atoms.

The instability of radioactive atoms is more complicated. We need to consider the total binding energy of nuclei—or perhaps we should say "unbinding energy," for it is defined as the energy required to separate a nucleus into free (isolated) protons, neutrons, and electrons. It is calculated as the difference between the actual mass of a given nucleus and the total mass of the free protons and free neutrons of which it consists. This difference in mass is expressed in atomic mass units or in energy units, usually in electron volts.

Note carefully that binding energy is the energy that a nucleus *does not have* in comparison to the total energy of its separate parts, and that this energy is measured in terms of differences in mass according to the equation $E = mc^2$. An examination of the periodic chart reveals that, as we pass from the lighter to the heavier elements, the ratio between the atomic weight and the atomic number increases. This means that the number of neutrons relative to the number of protons increases. It is also apparent that the *total binding energy* per nucleus is greater for the heavier elements simply because there are more particles to be held together (or isolated). The *binding energy per nucleon,* however, is about constant for the heavier elements. For the lighter elements the binding energy per nucleon increases rapidly up to nuclei of mass number of about 40. It increases more slowly up to elements of mass numbers of about 55 to 60, changes little in those with mass numbers between 60 and 70, and then very slowly increases for the rest of the elements with higher mass numbers (Fig. 41).

Note that the greater the binding energy, the more energy per nucleon needed to break a nucleus up into its constituent nucleons. Note also that iron, a "base" metal, has the greatest binding energy per nucleon of all elements, which means that it is the most stable. Others with about the same binding energy as iron are manganese,

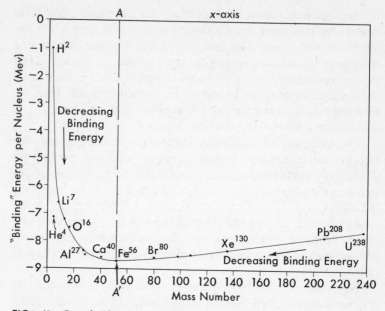

FIG. 41. *Graph Showing Binding Energy per Nucleon Plotted against Mass Numbers.* Only a few stable, or near-stable, isotopes are shown. Note that the binding energy per nucleon (not total binding energy of the nucleus) is almost constant for elements with mass numbers greater than $Al.^{27}$ The distance between the curve and the x-axis (top of diagram) is proportional to the energy per nucleon that would be required to take the nucleus apart. Note that this distance is greatest in Fe^{56} (the distance AA'). Thus the curve is concave upward from a minimum at mass number 56. This means that more energy is required to take the nucleus of iron apart than for any other element.

cobalt, nickel, copper, and zinc. These elements have the most stable nuclei, and therefore are least likely to be broken up, i.e., fissioned. Note that in Fig. 41 the arrows alongside the curve both point downward toward the low point of the curve. This means that to attain greater binding energy per nucleus, the heavier elements must disintegrate, either by emitting nucleons in the form of alpha particles or by fissioning. It also means that the lighter elements must fuse to form heavier elements if greater binding energy per nucleon is to be attained. *In either case energy is released* by some amount of matter being converted into energy. This follows from the definition of binding energy. The amount released is greatest when twenty-six protons and thirty neutrons combine to form iron.

The graph shown in Fig. 41 gives us a clue to the reason for the limit to the number of naturally occurring elements. All of the naturally radioactive elements are at the right in the graph, and all those at the right of the graph are radioactive. If there ever were any elements heavier than uranium 92, they must have been very unstable, and so have long since disintegrated. Eleven elements beyond atomic number 92 have been artificially created by man; all are highly unstable, with extremely short half-lives compared to the age of the earth. If they ever existed they have long since decayed either to the radioactive elements we find naturally or to stable lead.

Another clue to the stability of nuclei may be found in the relative numbers of protons and neutrons they contain. In the lighter elements the number of neutrons equals the number of protons. In iron the number of neutrons is 15 per cent larger than the number of protons; in lead the number is just over 50 per cent, and in uranium there are 58.7 per cent more neutrons than protons in the nucleus. Seemingly, the more protons in the nucleus, the more neutrons necessary to maintain stability, and when the number of protons rises above eighty-two (that of nonradioactive lead), no number of neutrons can counteract the repulsive effect of the protons for one another. It may be that the neutrons act as a sort of nuclear cement to hold the nucleons together. Isotopes with an even number of protons and an even number of neutrons seem to be more stable than those with an odd number of one and an even number of the other, and the latter are, in their turn, more stable than those with an odd number of each.

We will conclude this section on stability of the nucleus by stating that whatever the attraction between neutrons and protons may be, it appears to be very strong at extremely short distances but extremely weak at any other distance, much more so than is the case with gravitational or electrostatic forces.

From this discussion and from the binding-energy curve (Fig. 41) there emerge the two methods by which energy may be released quickly and in large amounts from the nuclei. One is through the disintegration of the heavier atoms, i.e., by fission, and the other is by combination of lighter elements to form heavier ones, i.e., by fusion. We will now turn our attention to them.

Nuclear Fission

From the discussions it is apparent that nuclear physicists realized that large amounts of energy are stored within the atom, and that this energy is emitted spontaneously from the nuclei of certain atoms of high atomic weight during radioactivity. The problem was to learn how to release this energy and to control it. The search for the means to obtain nuclear energy and bring it under control was not, as so many people believe, prompted by a desire to develop an atomic bomb during World War II. Rather, it followed from the sequence of events that began with the discoveries of Becquerel, the Curies, Thomson, Einstein, and Rutherford in the 1890's and early 1900's. The wartime researchers merely did on an enormous scale what scientists in their research laboratories had been doing on a small scale. Actually the war brought about little new fundamental research; i.e., few additions to basic knowledge were made. Scientists were much too busy hastening to put to practical use the knowledge they already had.

The discovery of the neutron gave the nuclear physicists a new "bullet" with which to bombard atoms. The neutron has about the same mass as the proton and about one-fourth that of the alpha particle. It has one great advantage over either in that it could penetrate into the nuclei of atoms, scoring direct hits, because it has no charge and so experiences no repulsion. Neutrons are ejected from some *artificially* radioactive atoms at high speeds. A typical reaction was that caused by bombarding boron with alpha particles. A radioactive isotope of nitrogen and a neutron were produced:

$$_5B^{10} + _2He^4 \rightarrow _7N^{13} + _0n^1$$

They lose energy in passing through matter only by direct collisions. In some of these collisions the neutrons will be absorbed or captured by nuclei, especially after they have been slowed down. A neutron captured by a nucleus adds one nucleon to it, thus creating a new isotope. Isotopes that are not found in nature are always unstable—which is the reason that they are not found in nature.

Once a source of neutrons had been established, they were used to bombard other atoms. Fermi bombarded uranium with them in 1934; Hahn and Strassman, in early 1938. Presumably they obtained fission, but it was not recognized as such until early in 1939. The fission was found to result in the formation of two elements near the middle of the periodic table, barium and krypton, or antimony and niobium, or strontium and xenon, etc. In all cases the atomic numbers of the two elements add up to ninety-two, but their mass numbers are always larger than those of their stable isotopes; i.e., they contain excess neutrons and so are radioactive. It is these radioactive isotopes that constitute the "fall-out" from nuclear explosions. A typical fission reaction is

$$_{92}U^{235} + {}_0n^1 \rightarrow {}_{92}U^{236} \rightarrow$$
$$_{54}Xe^{140} + {}_{38}Sr^{94} + 2{}_0n^1 + \text{gamma ray} + 200 \text{ Mev}$$

U^{235} is the only isotope of uranium that can be fissioned by low-energy neutrons. This isotope is present in natural uranium only in the proportion of 1 to 140. In every case a number of neutrons are produced by fission, the average number per fissioned atom being 2.5. This means that the reaction can be self-sustaining; i.e., neutrons from the outside are not needed to keep it going. A chain reaction would be possible if not too many neutrons escaped to the outside or were absorbed. (A chain reaction is like a chain letter, with which you are all doubtless familiar.) (See Fig. 42.) The amount of U^{235} in ordinary uranium (U^{238}) is not enough to start a chain reaction; too many neutrons are absorbed by the U^{238}. It is therefore necessary to separate them. This cannot be done chemically, because all isotopes of the same element behave exactly alike in chemical reactions. Two methods were developed, both based on the difference in mass numbers, and both very expensive. When they had these methods, scientists could develop the atomic bomb.

If the mass of U^{235} is below a certain critical size, the chain reaction will not take place; too many neutrons escape to the outside without causing fission. Conversely, if the mass is above the critical size, the chain reaction operates spontaneously, and the bomb explodes instantly. The problem is to control the chain reac-

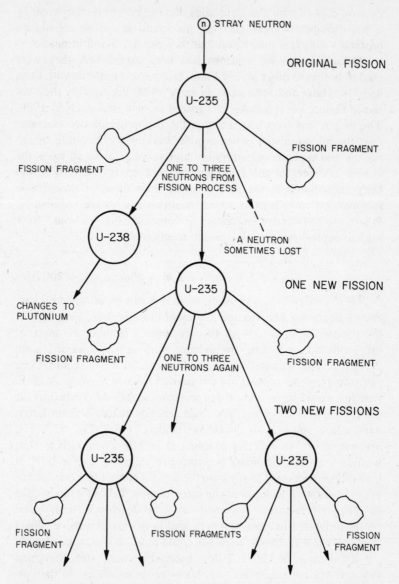

STRAY NEUTRON

ORIGINAL FISSION

U-235

FISSION FRAGMENT

FISSION FRAGMENT

ONE TO THREE
NEUTRONS FROM
FISSION PROCESS

U-238

A NEUTRON
SOMETIMES LOST

CHANGES TO
PLUTONIUM

U-235

ONE NEW FISSION

FISSION FRAGMENT

ONE TO THREE
NEUTRONS AGAIN

FISSION FRAGMENT

TWO NEW FISSIONS

U-235

U-235

FISSION
FRAGMENT

FISSION FRAGMENTS

FISSION
FRAGMENT

FIG. 42. *A Chain Reaction.* The release of several new neutrons causes additional fissions.

tion. This is done by separating the U^{235} into two or more parts, each part a bit below the critical size. To set the bomb off, all that has to be done is to bring the parts together. No source of neutrons is necessary to start the reaction because cosmic rays are constantly creating neutrons in the atmosphere. Despite their half-life of thirteen minutes, there are always enough neutrons around to start the reaction. The temperature generated in the heart of the bomb is enormous—many millions of degrees centigrade. The maximum size of the A-bomb is strictly limited by the number of masses of fissionable material, each below the critical size, that can be brought together at the same instant to form a single mass above critical size. Only a small part of each atom of U^{235} is converted into energy; i.e., only the energy representing the difference between the mass of the uranium atom and the combined masses of the products is released. The amount per gram of mass converted is given by $E = mc^2$.

If we examine the graph (Fig. 41), we can see that the fission products with their mass numbers around 90 and 140 are nearer the base of the curve than uranium. This is always true. It is therefore not possible to fission elements at the low part of the curve. Several of the other radioactive elements, notably Th^{233}, can be fissioned under proper circumstances.[14]

Atomic Fusion

The discovery of atomic fission put a new light on the source of the energy radiated from the sun. It had long been known that the enormous energy radiated could not possibly be accounted for by normal chemical processes. Could it be that atoms were being fissioned in the sun? Analysis of the sun's spectrum reveals compara-

[14] The most important fissionable atom is plutonium 239, an element that does not occur in nature but which is made synthetically by bombarding U^{238} with neutrons. Plutonium is radioactive, but since it has a half-life of about 24,000 years it is stable enough to be usable. It is fissionable just as is U^{235}. It is "made" in an atomic pile under controlled conditions. Unlike U^{235} it can be separated from U^{238} by chemical means, for it is a different element.

tively few atoms that are fissionable, whereas it reveals large amounts of hydrogen and helium. Inspection of the curve in Fig. 41 shows that these could not be produced by fission of larger atoms. The curve does, however, suggest that the elements to the left of the low point of the curve might be fused to form elements whose energy per nucleon is greater than either of the elements to be fused.

It was in 1939 that Bethe of Cornell proposed the carbon cycle (so-called because carbon serves as a sort of nuclear catalyst) to account for the source of the sun's energy. In this cycle, hydrogen is converted into helium. Later, the conversion of hydrogen to helium by another method was worked out on paper. It was this method that made the hydrogen bomb possible. The details about the bomb are not available, but we can make an educated guess.

As mentioned, there are two isotopes of hydrogen in addition to ordinary hydrogen, $_1H^2$ (deuterium) and $_1H^3$ (tritium). Deuterium is a naturally occurring variety. About one molecule in every 6,700 contains deuterium rather than ordinary hydrogen. Its separation is thus expensive. Tritium is radioactive, but its half-life is 12.5 years and so it may be stored for a time. It is very rare in nature but can be transmuted from lithium at a very high cost. This reaction is

$$\text{lithium} \quad + \quad \text{a neutron} \quad \rightarrow \quad \text{tritium} \quad + \quad \text{helium}$$

$$_3Li^6 \quad + \quad _0n^1 \quad \rightarrow \quad _1H^3 \quad + \quad _2He^4$$

The most probable reaction producing helium is

$$\text{deuterium} \quad + \quad \text{tritium} \quad \rightarrow \quad \text{helium} \quad + \quad \text{neutron} \quad + \quad \text{energy}$$

$$_1H^2 \quad + \quad _1H^3 \quad \rightarrow \quad _2He^4 \quad + \quad _0n^1 \quad + \quad 17.6 \text{ mev}$$

This needs a fantastically high temperature to activate it, 15,000,-000° C at least. This temperature can be obtained only by using an A-bomb. To make the H-bomb, a small A-bomb is surrounded by a quantity of liquefied deuterium and tritium, which in turn is surrounded by a quantity of LiH^2. The "firing" of the A-bomb supplies the heat to start the fusion reaction. Since the activation energy of the fusion process is so extremely high, there is no upper limit to the size of the H-bomb, except perhaps due to technical difficulties; i.e., there is no critical size as there is with the A-bomb.

Bombs equivalent to 50,000,000 tons of TNT have been exploded. Any radioactive fall-out from the H-bomb is due entirely to the A-bomb used to trigger it.

Note that the most usable energy that can be obtained from nuclear reactions of any kind is heat. Nuclear reactors (sometimes called "piles") are simply devices in which the fission (not fusion) of plutonium atoms is not allowed to reach chain-reaction proportions. The heat given off is used to heat water to run a steam engine which in turn runs a dynamo to generate electrical energy. Atomic reactors are very large and heavy, for they must be surrounded with several tons of shielding material to absorb the deadly radiations. There is no other way at present to use atomic power, nor is there likely to be—on a large scale. There is no way at present to use the energy of fusion, nor is the possibility at all promising.

CHAPTER 20

Conclusion

We have completed our story of man's investigations into the structure of atoms insofar as it can be told to an educated layman. We have also delved to some small degree into the structure of *molecules,* because it was not possible to do otherwise: the properties of most forms of matter with which we are familiar are not those of individual atoms composing them but of their molecules. The time has now come to look back on the way we have come and forward to see what the future may hold.

We reviewed briefly the development of physical science from the time of Thales of Miletus to Robert Boyle—from the sixth century B.C. to the end of the seventeenth century A.D.—largely to show the dependence of scientific progress on the existence of fruitful theories to guide man's investigations. We began with Thales because he was the first, insofar as we know, to break away from the mythological traditions which had their roots in supernatural explanations for physical phenomena. He assumed that the universe is natural and potentially explainable by man without resort to the supernatural.[1] He believed, as every scientist must, in a universe where law and order prevail rather than in a universe subject to the whims of some god or goddess.

The Greek theory that all matter is composed of various combinations of four elements, earth, air, fire, and water, and is therefore continuous, proved not to be fruitful. It resulted in little progress in understanding the fundamental nature of matter during the more than two thousand years of its acceptance. Compare this

[1] Einstein once remarked that the most incomprehensible thing about the universe is that it is comprehensible to man.

196

with the great accomplishments made in the hundred and fifty years following the acceptance of Dalton's atomic theory in the early 1800's. True enough, this theory has been modified; divisibility of the atom has been substituted for indivisibility. This modification no more constitutes a rejection of Dalton's theory than the differences between modern automobiles and those of 1910 constitute a rejection of the fundamental principles governing their operation. Insofar as the science of chemistry is concerned, it is the divisibility of atoms into electrons and nuclei that is important. The divisibility of the nucleus has mattered little—except to the nuclear physicist, to whom it is all important.

A fruitful theory does not come from the wild blue yonder, but commonly appears as an integrating concept sequential to many observations and experiments made by many investigators. Science is cumulative; one thing commonly leads to another rather than to a dead end. Physical science may be likened to an endless series of connecting rooms in each of which there are at least two main locked doors, one at each end; there may or may not be locked side doors to other rooms. In places the main series divides into two, or three, or sometimes more, subsidiary series of rooms, all with locked doors. Some of these subsidiary series lead one to a dead end; it connects up with no other room. Some of them join together again to form a main series once more, but not for long. Another division into subsidiary series takes place, and so on forever. To progress ever forward, one must progress from room to room in the proper sequence, and he must have the correct keys. The theories of science are the keys, and the measure of a theory is the number of doors that it will unlock. A really bad theory will provide the key to only one or two doors, and these are commonly side doors into rooms that are dead ends. A better theory will unlock more doors in the main sequence, perhaps some side doors also. The more fruitful the theory, the better the key. Even so, a door will be reached that cannot be opened by it. A new key must be provided, either by a completely new theory, or by a significant modification of the old. Some rooms have two main exit doors into other rooms; a theory may unlock one but not the other. The pathways of science are strewed with discarded keys, keys that were used to unlock some doors but which failed with others.

Needless to say, no one scientist provides all these keys. Many, perhaps scores, perhaps hundreds, are involved in the search for the proper keys, some taking up where the others have left off. For every one who is successful in finding a key, there are hundreds or even thousands who have contributed their bit, if only to indicate areas where the key may *not* be found.

Thus a proper concept of the process of combustion was the key that led to the law of conservation of mass, the law of definite proportions, the law of multiple proportions, and shortly to the atomic theory of Dalton, which integrated them all—and provided the key to many more. It could not, however, unlock the door to the law of combining volumes, and this remained a problem for fifty years. Then Cannizzaro removed it by resurrecting the suggestion made by Avogadro (Chapter 6) shortly after the atomic theory was first formulated. The key provided by this suggestion would not have worked, however, if another seemingly unrelated line of investigation had not taken place. This line began in the study of work and energy. Although to us it is apparent that heat and mechanical energy are related via steam engines, it is by no means obvious that heat is a form of energy rather than a material substance; it took long and careful work to prove the relationship. This investigation into the nature of heat introduced man to the world of molecules by way of a study of gases, and finally led to another great integrating concept, the kinetic-molecular theory of matter. The key provided by this theory enabled the two series of rooms to be connected again. Aided greatly by Mendeleev's periodic table, rapid advancement was once more possible.

Eventually two doors were reached which could not be unlocked by any key available at the time. The problems were not new, for they had long been building up. They arose from investigations into two apparently unrelated aspects of matter. One came from the discovery that matter was unquestionably electrical in nature. Michael Faraday made quantitative measurements of these electrical charges but left unsolved the manner in which they were associated with atoms. The other arose out of the quite different problem of spectra, especially bright line spectra. It was intimately tied up with the origin of light. That light was a wave motion had been indisputably proved in the very early 1800's. Maxwell's electromagnetic theory (*ca.* 1865) was a great step forward, for it showed how light could be transmitted from sun and stars through empty space and without loss of energy. It provided the key to some side doors but left the main ones still locked, for it provided no answer to the problem of spectra.

In the late 1890's two new discoveries spelled the final doom of the old belief in the indivisibility of the atom. These were the discovery of radioactivity and of the electron. Very shortly, Max Planck made matters worse by reluctantly putting forth the quantum theory of radiation. Einstein's use of it in the photon theory of light seemed like a step backward, for no one could see how the electromagnetic theory could be given up, or how the two theories could be reconciled. Ten years later Rutherford put forth his nuclear theory of atoms. All of these theories provided keys, but none would unlock the main doors, doors which had to be opened if man was to understand the fundamental nature of atoms. There was critical need for another of those great integrating theories, one which would integrate the origin of light, spectra, photons, electrons, and their relations to atoms.

Such a theory was Bohr's theory of the hydrogen atom. Much work remained to be done, however. In the process Bohr's original theory was altered almost beyond recognition before it could be successfully applied to atoms other than hydrogen. Once modified, in addition to integrating the phenomena already mentioned, it explained the behavior of atoms in chemical reactions, explained the periodicities in the periodic table, and laid the basis for understanding the physical and chemical properties of all of the elements. The electronic theory of chemical bonding provided the "final" explanation of the chemical behavior of all kinds of atoms. The word *final* is in quotes because we can never really know whether or not any explanation is truly final.

Investigations into the nature of the nucleus inevitably followed its discovery. The method was to bombard atoms with alpha particles (helium ions) ejected from radioactive atoms. When protons were discovered they were used as "bullets." However, when neutrons came to light they proved to be better bullets for some purposes than either alpha particles or protons. The two chief discoveries were the artificial transmutation of certain atoms into other kinds of atoms, and the accidental discovery of atomic fission by bombardment of U^{235} atoms with neutrons. Atomic fusion was, however, no accident; it was considered possible from mathematical considerations and needed only experiment to prove it. Further bombardment of atoms by atomic particles given very high velocities in various atom-smashing machines broke protons and neutrons in various ways to produce many other particles. We need not concern ourselves with them, for they play no part in our story.

Atoms with more than eighty-two protons in their nuclei are unstable; they break down into other atoms radioactively. All known atoms have an integral number of protons. From these two facts it can be concluded that the periodic table of the elements now contains all of the various kinds of atoms that make up the whole universe. This conclusion is supported by evidence from the spectra of thousands of stars. *They show only "fingerprints" of elements found here on earth.*

One of the most recent rooms to be unlocked is that which holds the new and amazing science of solid-state physics. Its key was discovered via the investigations which led to the invention of the transistor, that tiny substitute for vacuum tubes in radios and hearing aids. Solid-state physics is the study of solid matter apart from liquids and gases. Strictly speaking, there is no such thing as solid matter, for Rutherford (p. 88) proved that the atom was mostly empty space. The nuclei of even the largest atoms are inconceivably small, so small that a billion billion of them, if closely packed, would be invisible to the naked eye. However, they are not closely packed, but are arranged in more or less intricate geometric patterns in which the distances between a nucleus and its neighbors are extremely large compared to their sizes. The empty spaces between nuclei are occupied by varying numbers of revolving electrons, 92 per nucleus in the case of uranium, the most massive of naturally occurring atoms. These whirling electrons, moving at incredible speeds, have so much space in which to move that collisions do not occur at anything like normal temperatures. Nature, using arrangements of this sort, makes things in almost infinite variety, hard or soft, brittle or malleable, porous or dense, flexible or rigid, electrically conductive or not, etc. The pursuit of explanations of the above has led to the discovery of some amazing properties of certain elements, particularly those that are borderline between metals and nonmetals, and so are neither good electrical conductors nor good insulators. They are called semiconductors. Scores of the products of solid-state physics are already in use, in transistor radios, in artificial satellites, rockets and missiles, and many other devices. The possibilities go far beyond the limits of ordinary electronics; they are so fantastically large that they stagger the imagination. As we have said before, new knowledge begets new knowledge and so on ad infinitum.

Throughout this book we have emphasized theories and laws rather than the practical side of science. There is little intellectual discipline in the latter, little that will help you see further and more dispassionately in other fields. If you now think back about the scientists mentioned in this book, you will not be able to find one of them who was trying to invent anything of practical value at the time he made his discovery. This is not to say that none of them invented anything. Perhaps they did, but, if so, none of them is remembered because of that. We stress the value of what has been called "useless" science over that of practical science, simply because the practical scientist, e.g., Edison, depends almost wholly on "useless" science for his ideas. The hall of scientific fame is replete with the names of men who made facts significant, men who integrated them into conceptual schemes, but contains the names of few men who were mere discoverers of facts. No practical scientist ever won a Nobel prize.

Because the fruits of science have been used to make devastating weapons, many people are inclined to blame the scientist for these weapons. "Why did they have to invent the bomb?" they ask. The work on the structure of the atom began as a purely intellectual endeavor. No one could know where it would lead. Once atomic fission was discovered the bomb was inevitable if the political climate was ripe for it. Those who blame scientists for *not* refusing to work on the bomb should ask themselves the question, "What would I think of our scientists who refused if Hitler's scientists went on to develop it first?"

What of the future? Will scientists ever solve all of the mysteries of the universe? No scientist really thinks so. The solution of every problem creates new problems. The ignorant have no conception of what they do not know; the learned are humble because they know so little. Will our present theories all be overthrown someday, to be replaced by different ones? Some will, some will undergo revision, and some will stand pretty much as they are. In general, the older theories stand the best chance of retention intact.

The laws, however, will always hold within the limits placed upon them. Newton's laws of motion apply today just as they always have.

One of the outstanding differences between the science of today and that before World War II is its relation to the public. Science can no longer be considered the business of scientists only. It has become everybody's business. Let us forget for a moment about the bomb. What the scientists do in the next few decades will have an important influence on the lives of all, for science has now become a great natural resource which will probably change the lives of many of us. Can an intelligent citizen afford to be ignorant of science? Can he afford to leave the use to be made of scientific discoveries to men who are ignorant of science and its methods? Or can he afford to leave the decisions for such use even to scientists themselves? The only alternative is for every intelligent citizen to become familiar with science and its methods. If this book has given its readers some such familiarity, then it has accomplished the purpose for which it was written.

INDEX

(The superscript n indicates a reference to a footnote.)

Acceleration, 71^n, 91^n
Alchemy, 8, 11, 28
Alpha particle, 82, 87, 170, 181, 183: scattering of, 89, 90; stability of, 186^n
Alternating current, 42, 81^n
Anaximenes, 7
Antimatter, 174^n
Anode, 57
Argon, 148^n
Aristotle, 7, 8, 9, 24
Arrhenius, Svante, 61^n
Atom, 9, 21, 39: divisibility of, 69; weight of, 26
Atomic fission, 190: fusion, 193; mass number, 173; mass unit, 183^n; number, 146; ratios, 27; reactor, 195
Atomic size, 26, 165
Atomic theory, Dalton's, 21: nuclear, 86
Atomic weights, 13, 13^n, 24–26
Avogadro, Amadeus, 19, 29, 32
Avogadro's law, 30, 31
Avogadro's number, 26
Bacon, Roger, 11
Balmer's formula, 126–127, 144
Becquerel, Henri, 82
Beta ray, 82, 178
Battery, chemical, 56, 57
Binding energy, 187–188
Bohr, Niels, 135
Bohr theory, 137–146
Bond, chemical, 167^n
Boyle, Robert, 12
Boyle's law, 50^n
Broglie, Louis de, 152
Cannizzaro, Stanislaus, 32
Carbon dating, 180
Cathode, 57: ray, 72
Chain reaction, 191, 192
Charge, on nucleus, 146, 147
Charges, negative, 40: positive, 40
Chemical bond, 167^n
Chemical reaction, 18: essence of, 165
Classification, 13^n
Cockcroft-Walton experiment, 183–185
Combining volumes, law of, 21, 29–32
Compound, 11, 12, 33
Conductors, 41, 42, 81
Copernicus, 11
Cosmic rays, 173^n
Coulomb, 62^n
Count Rumford, 35, 35^n
Critical size, 191–192
Curie, Marie, 82
Dalton, John, 19, 21, 29, 31
de Broglie, Louis, 152
Definite proportions, law of, 19, 20
Democritus, 8, 9

Deuterium, 186, 194
Diffraction, wave, 102–103
Direct current, 81^n
Dispersion, of light, 98, 99
$E = mc^2$, 151, 182
e/m, 73–77
Earth, age of, 180
Eddington, Arthur S., 137^n
Edison, Thomas, 79, 80^n
Einstein, Albert, 129, 130, 131^n
Electric current, 81
Electric "eye," 132^n
Electric field, 75^n
Electricity, current, 42: static, 42
Electrodes, 57
Electrolysis, 58–66: law of, 66
Electrolyte, 58^n
Electromagnetic theory, 110–114: waves, 95, 113; waves, model of, 112–113; model of, 112, 113
Electron, charge on, 68, 85: defined, 58; discovery of, 69; distribution of, 91; mass of, 78, 85; spin of, 160
Electron volt, 181, 181^n: wavelength of, 154, 154^n
Electronic configuration of atoms, 164
Elements, 11–13: classification of, 16, 17; definition of, 11, 12, 169, 171; primary, 7–9; transmutation of, 170, 171, 178
Equations, chemical, 18: nuclear, 172^n
Erg, 182
Ether, luminiferous, 110
ev, 181, 181^n
Exclusion principle, 150, 159
Facts, defined, 49
Families, chemical, 13
Faraday, Michael, 56, 56^n, 110
Faraday's law of electrolysis, 65
Fission, nuclear, 190
Forces, molecular, 35^n, 39^n
Formulas, chemical, 18
Franklin, Benjamin, 40–41
Frequency, 96, 99, 114: threshold, 131
Fusion, nuclear, 193
Galileo, 11: law of free fall, 50^n
Gamma rays, 82
Gas discharge tube, 70
Gas pressure, 38^n
Gasses, 29, 33: diatomic, 34; inert, 163, 164; monatomic, 34
Gram-atomic weights, 25
Gram-atomic molecular weights, 26^n
Heisenberg's uncertainty principle, 155
Helium, 84, 84^n, 160: nucleus, mass of, 185
Hertz, Heinrich, 114

Huygens, Christian, 107
Hydrogen, 25, 26, 160
Hypothesis, 48–49
Ions, 33^n: discovery of, 60
Isotopes, 175, 177
Insulators, 41, 42
Joule, James, 35, 42
Kepler, Johannes, 11
Kinetic energy, 36^n
Kinetic-molecular theory, 33–39
Lambda (λ), 96^n
Lavosier, Antoine, 12, 18, 42
Law, combining volumes, 21, 29: conservation of mass, 18; definite proportions, 19, 20; electrolysis, 66; free fall, 50^n; multiple proportions, 20
Laws, scientific, 49–50
m/e, 78
Magnetic field, 72^n
Mass, law of conservation of, 18
Matter, electrical nature of, 40: subdivision of, 18
Mendeleev, Dmitri, 14
Mev, 181^n
Michelson, Albert A., 55, 108–109
Molecules, 26, 33, 39: motions of, 11^n
Momentum, 138^n
Moseley, Henry G.-J., 147
Motion, random, 36, 36^n, 39^n
Multiple proportions, law of, 20
n, 142, 142^n, 143
Neutron, 148, 171–172: stability of, 186
Newton, Isaac, 11, 98^n, 107
Nuclear energy, 181: fission, 190; fusion, 193; reactions, 172^n
Nuclei, stability of, 186–190
Nucleon, 173
Nucleus, diameter of, 91: discovery of, 90; structure of, 169
Orbits, permitted, 138, 153: stable, 138
Oxygen, theory of combustion, 19
Pair production, 173
Parallax, 6^n
Particulate, 135^n
Pauli, Wolfgang, 151, 159
Periodic law, 14: table, 13, 14, 159–168
Phlogiston theory, 18
Philosophy, Greek, 5, 6, 9
Photoelectric effect, 129–132
Photon theory, 129–134
Planck, Max, 127, 129
Planck's constant, 128
Plutonium, 193^n
Poincaré, Henri, 53
Polarization, 105
Positive rays, 70, 175
Positron, 173
Powers of 10, 26^n
Proton, 148, 171, 186
Prout, Williams, 85, 174, 175

Pythagoras, 7
Quantum, 128
Quantum numbers, 142^n, 150–151, 156–159
Radioactivity, as time clock, 180: discovery of, 82, 84; explanation of, 177–179; half-life, 179
Rays, 72^n: alpha, 82–84; beta, 82–84; gamma, 82–84, 119; infrared, 117; ultraviolet, 117
Reactions, chemical, 165: nuclear, 172^n
Recombination of ions, 70
Refraction, 98
Relative weights, 25
Relativity, 149^n
Roemer, Olaf, 108
Roentgen, Wilhelm, 118
Rumford, Count, 42
Rutherford, Ernest (Lord), 84, 128
Schroedinger, Edwin, 155, 155^n
Science, definition of, 52, 53: fundamental, 54; practical, 54; pure, 54
Scientific method, 51
Semiconductor, 200
Shells, atomic, 158, 160–165
Spectra, 115, 120–126: atomic, 15, 124; bright line, 123; continuous, 120, 143^n; flame, 124; problems of, 124
Spectroscope, 122
Spectrum, 99
Stoney, Johnstone, 66
Subshells, 158, 160–164
Symbols, chemical, 18
Thales, 6, 40
Theories, general, 8, 45–48, 197
Thermionic emission, 79–81, 132^n
Thomson, Joseph J. (Sir), 74
Transformation, energy to matter, 173: matter to energy, 173, 183–185
Transistor, 200
Transmutation of element, 170–171, 178
Tritium, 194
Uncertainty principle, 153
Uranium, 182, 191–193
Valence, 27, 28
van Helmont, 11
Velocity selector, 175^n
Voltaic cell, 56, 57
Wave, crest, 95: longitudinal, 104; mechanical theory, 155; motion, 93; refraction, 97, 98; sound, 104; trough, 95
Wave vs. particle, 152–155
Wavelength, 95
Waves, electromagnetic, 95
Waves, light, 92–105: mechanical, 95; radio, 117; velocity of, 96
X-ray spectra, 147
X-rays, discovery of, 118, 146–147
Young, Thomas, 107